D0730116

BLOOD

American Museum Science Books are published for The American Museum of Natural History by The Natural History Press. Directed by a joint editorial board made up of members of the staff of the Museum and Doubleday, this series is an extension of the Museum's scientific and educational activities, making available to the student and general reader inexpensive, up-to-date, and reliable books in the life and earth sciences, including anthropology and astronomy. The Natural History Press is a division of Doubleday & Company, Inc., and has its editorial offices at The American Museum of Natural History, Central Park West at 79th Street, New York, New York 10024, and its business offices at 501 Franklin Avenue, Garden City, New York 11238.

BLOOD

LEO VROMAN

American Museum Science Books
PUBLISHED FOR
THE AMERICAN MUSEUM OF NATURAL HISTORY

THE NATURAL HISTORY PRESS
GARDEN CITY, NEW YORK

*BLOOD is also available in The Natural
History Press hardcover edition.*

AMERICAN MUSEUM SCIENCE BOOKS EDITION: 1968
COPYRIGHT © 1967 BY LEO VROMAN
ALL RIGHTS RESERVED
PRINTED IN THE UNITED STATES OF AMERICA

CONTENTS

INTRODUCTION

The last jungles in the world seem to withdraw almost eagerly from advancing man. The forests drain themselves of beasts and flatten into meadows, the meadows are turned into suburbs, and the suburbs are swallowed by our cities. The only thriving wildlife still barely touched by man is the hot, confusing, and poorly lit world within himself. I am a nature lover; but maybe for lack of larger scenery, I have learned to enjoy the tabletop-size scenery inside me, and inside you of course. The strangely shaped glands, and bones, the transparent lungs, the madly dense tangle of cells in the brain hold worlds within worlds; and, through it all and always, streams the blood.

Most of us, while very young, learned not to admire the beauty of blood, but rather to hate the pain that always appeared with it; and the pain taught us to hate the sight of blood itself, convincing us that blood must stay where it belongs. It still makes us startle at anything red. Well, there is little reason left for this fear: we know now that we can make new blood of our own quite fast, or borrow someone else's even faster—but the fear lingers on, even in those who must give or take only a tiny part of this alarming treasure.

I drew my first sample of blood after the war. I had

begun to work for a pathologist, Dr. Sylvan E. Moolten, at St. Peter's Hospital in New Brunswick, New
Jersey, where I was to study the function of blood
platelets. I was not well prepared. I had learned as a
student that platelets are small particles coming from
cells that live in the bone marrow; these were the particles, in those days and books, that were thought to
make blood clot. To this, Dr. Moolten, always kind
enough to think I knew more than I confessed, added
a large number of facts and thoughts, mostly within
the hour it took the train to bring us from New York.
The train was noisy and the words were long; some
of them may have applied to the landscape passing
by, and though I can now and often do say "mega-
karyocytes" or "polycythemia," I still may have re-
tained a few medical terms that sound suspiciously
like "Rahway" and "Metuchen." Meanwhile, on the
practical side, I learned in the hospital which journals
and articles to read and which ones not to read. I saw
the brave and flippant young technicians going up-
stairs with empty tubes and coming down with tubes
full of blood. I watched them making smears (the
trick of spreading a small drop of blood over a glass
microscope slide so that all cells will dry side by side;
it takes a second to do and a year to learn). Soon I
could even stain their smears about as well as they
did, flooding them with a mixture that turned the cell
bodies pinkish to pale purple and their nuclei dark.
But it took months of urging myself to take a syringe
in my own hands and approach a real man with it,
even if he was a patient safely down sick.

Unlike the machine gun, the syringe is an awesome
weapon to hold, because it forces the attacker so close
to his victim, who will then look at him and think:
What do you think you are doing? It is easier to kill

a distant crowd with a missile than to prick a child with a pin.

My first victim was an old man. I tied a length of thin rubber tubing around his quite human upper arm. I was so intent on smiling through it all like a ballerina that I was unable to announce my intention. I unwrapped the sterile glass syringe, sunk its plunger into its barrel, put it down, unplugged the tube containing the sterile needle, fit the needle onto the syringe, took a cotton ball out of its alcohol bath, and turned to the good man, who had already made a fist, and stretched his arm. Sticking a needle into someone's skin, like breaking an egg or dying, should be done quickly or it becomes a messy experience; I learned that at least. And I got my sample, and remembered to pull off the tourniquet, though I forgot to stop smiling until I had returned to the lab.

If I had been as inexperienced a scientist as I was a technician, I would have felt that the bit of living matter I had more or less painlessly removed from a human being could now blindly live on as if it had never left home. But as a biologist I have learned mainly that if something alive is normally invisible, it will become quite abnormal as soon as it is made visible. If you want to see an earthworm as it normally lives, you must look at it only when it is gone. And that is even more true for any part of an organism. This leaves us rather helpless: we cannot understand the whole beast until we understand the parts, but we cannot even find the parts until we break up the whole, and thus change the life of the parts. To make biology even harder, life may be most active and specific where the skins of two structures meet, right at surfaces that our eyes and knife are inclined to separate. Nothing, for example, looks smoother and simpler than the inside walls of our blood vessels. Yet, as soon as the blood must leave these containers, it undergoes a physical and chemical revolution that we can only prevent by killing it a little bit. Some of this struggle against nature to understand nature is described in the first chapter.

CONTACT

We have left our hero in the Introduction with a syringe full of blood. What next? If he keeps it in the syringe or puts it in a glass test tube, it will turn into a solid mass within five to fifteen minutes. An hour or so later, this clot will appear to have shrunk to a smaller, darker red replica of itself (if the donor was healthy), and this retracted clot will be crouching in a self-made bath of clear pale yellow fluid, called serum.

I knew all this, of course; but when my very own first sample performed as it should, right in front of me, I felt as if I should have rewarded it. And especially since this clot retraction was said to be a function of the blood platelets, I felt as if it was trying to show me something that I should know. I wanted to have a closer look, and I began to spend time sitting behind a microscope looking one thousand times closer. The only space for research at that time was in the rabbit house, and there was only time enough at night. There I would sit, holding my left pinky tip with my left thumb and fingers to keep it from escaping my stabbing right hand in the dark. I would flatten a tiny drop of the blood between glass slide and coverslip, and look. Later, I bought a binocular phase microscope with wide angle oculars: binocular for both eyes, phase contrast to reveal transparent details (through this invention, water in air will look dark on white), and wide angle oculars so that looking in was no longer like looking through a narrow tube, but like falling out of the dark into a wide and bright and very foreign space.

The Structure of Blood

With the slide of live blood in place, nearly half of the world in there was taken by clear yellowish discs with thick edges: erythrocytes (red blood cells), sailing passively about in a clear liquid, called plasma (Figure 1). I could sometimes see the red cell surface

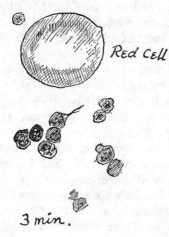

FIGURE 1

alive with a flickering hail of faint rings, like silent ponds hit by a fine and steady rain, and it was indeed a rain, but one of molecules large enough to make dents: protein most likely, and still too small to be seen when enlarged one thousand times. Between the erythrocytes I saw particles only about one-third as big as red cells: platelets at last, bouncing around a little as the plasma molecules hit them, but about half of them soon became stuck to the glass. And here and there, also stuck or still rolling around, were leukocytes (white blood cells), clear but structured almost like melting and freezing, roving, pale glass eyes.

In a drop of one cubic millimeter, which is about as big as the dot on an i, there are normally about five million red cells, three hundred thousand platelets,

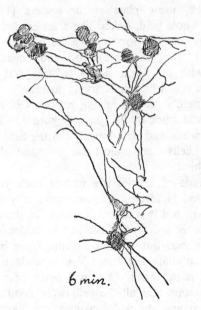

6 min.

FIGURE 2

and seven thousand white cells, but since their total volume is still a little less than half of all blood, they were spread out under the microscope with plenty of room between them to observe the plasma. For a few minutes, this space would seem void; then, as if a fog had lifted and they had always been there, fine lines would appear and cross each other like a sprinkle of hay: fibrin was forming (Figure 2).

Coagulation

The fibrin fibers, which had been formed by the grouping together of many molecules of a protein called fibrinogen, grew sturdier and formed a sloppy spider web, using platelets for spiders (Figure 3). Soon the whole field looked like a major disaster area, with many platelets forming blisters of more than ten times their size, that broke off and began to drift around, with the fibrin slowly twisting and contracting and a few white cells trying to crawl away from it all or merely grazing among remnants of fibrin and platelets still stuck to the glass (Figure 4). The fibrin clot meanwhile had withdrawn from the field, trapping most red cells and almost all platelets; the serum stayed behind.

Thousands of articles are written each year about things found in serum, because serum may not occur in our body, but it is so easy to make in the test tube: all you do is wait. To make instant coffee one must add hot water, but to make serum from blood one must add nothing but time. Yet, what is this handy serum? It is no longer (and will never be again) the original plasma that all the cells were floating around in before it was struck by coagulation (clotting), be-

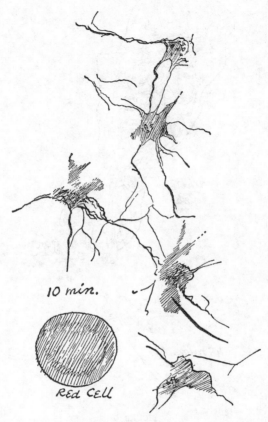

10 min.

RED CELL

FIGURE 3

cause the serum can never clot again. On the other hand, if you added a drop of fresh serum to a tube of freshly drawn blood, this blood would clot in a few seconds instead of in about ten minutes. This means that at least two things have happened in the mixture: 1. it made fibrin from something that existed first as invisibly dissolved material—fibrinogen;

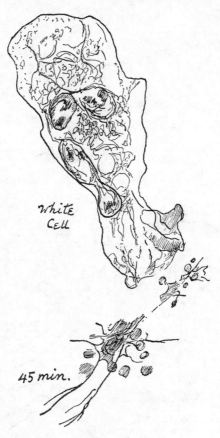

white
cell

45 min.

FIGURE 4

FIGURES 1–4: *These first four sketches are tracings made from preparations of my own blood. I had placed drops of fresh blood onto four glass slides, rinsed each off at the time indicated under each sketch, and fixed and stained what remained on the slides. Within three minutes, platelets had stuck to the glass and clumped; in six minutes, fibrin strands formed; in ten minutes, platelets "exploded"; and within forty-five minutes, white cells had crawled out of the clotted drop onto the slide, maybe eating all the way.*

2. something has formed, and remains in the serum, that can clot fibrinogen in seconds—but it took the blood ten minutes minus a few seconds to make this something, that we shall call thrombin. The thrombin, in turn, must have been formed from something that was not active, and we shall call that precursor prothrombin.

So there you have two reactions: after blood leaves the body, invisible prothrombin becomes converted to invisible thrombin, and, when enough thrombin has formed, it converts invisible fibrinogen into visible fibrin. The fibrinogen molecule is a big one; when dried, dead, blasted with metal dust that is intended to land like slanting sunlight, and finally enlarged about two hundred thousand times by the electron microscope, it can be seen as a thread with three beads on it. Thrombin probably chips a bit off two beads; the slightly damaged fibrinogen molecules, now called fibrin monomers (monomer = single parts), line up end to end and side by side to form the polymer (unit of many elements) called fibrin. Under the electron microscope, the lined-up monomer beads have been seen to result in fine stripes across the fibrin fibers.

Everything in this process, up to the time fibrin forms, is invisible. Just as if there were a one-team race of invisible relay runners, we can fire the starting shot and later see the ribbon move at the finish, but we cannot see who ran where or when. One thing we can do is put obstacles on various lengths of the track at various times. If we drag a wall across the track and run to the finish to see the ribbon still reached at the usual time, we can presume that the man had passed the location of the wall before we put it there. Or, to say this more scientifically: we can add an inhibitor at various times before fibrin formation, to find if the coagulation reactions have already been completed before the inhibitor against them had been added. Another thing we can do is run onto the track with a spray gun loaded with paint, and hope to hit the invisible runners. That way we can make them visible. But we also might hit them in the eyes, or hit other invisible people, and we may find out too late that we have been wasting our time following an innocent family to the picnic grounds with our paint on their backs, while the runners are running blindly and wild. Or, more scientifically: we may try to tag the proteins involved by using fluorescent dyes or radioactivity. However, since we cannot yet purify these proteins completely, we will not know how specific, how well aimed our tag will be or how it will mislead us—and we do not know if the tag will affect the reaction to be studied.

Thus far, the obstacle scheme has been the most attractive. The beginner, even if he does not plan to stamp out hemophilia and heart disease at once, feels urged to do something that at least affects the duration of the invisible period; and nothing is easier. Too much salt, too little salt, too much or too little acidity, anything that you might put into vegetable soup, will prolong the clotting time, except certain components of margarine maybe, which will hasten it. One of the nicest effects can be obtained by adding some chemical that removes the calcium dissolved in the blood. A bit of sodium oxalate or citrate will do the trick: decalcified blood does not clot and will allow us a reasonable period of time to play with it; the blood will clot a few minutes after we add the proper amount of calcium chloride back to it. Sadly enough, this like other things does not quite undo what we did, because we do not know exactly where and how the normal blood calcium spends its time; so we may be taking it away in some natural state and then adding a quite different form. We must not expect a chicken to be happy if we pluck it first and then throw a rug over it; still, we have to start somewhere, and the easier step may be the most rewarding.

Let us say then that you are standing in my lab, and that you have received a research grant to find out about the effect of surfaces upon blood coagulation. You have also received a bottle of decalcified blood that is so freshly drawn that most of the warm contents have hardly had time to come into contact with the walls of the bottle. What will you want to do, and can I help? As you can see from the blank space below, I plan to give you time to think.

One way of starting is to take a sheet of paper, draw a small picture of a bottle of blood near the upper edge in the middle and several lines like rays spreading down from it. This indicates that you are going to split the bottle contents in so many parts: for each part you must plan something different, and write or sketch that at the end of each short line. Let us call each part A, B, and C. Sample A can have, say, three lines leading down from it; call them A1, A2, and A3. Let me also point to the thing in my lab that looks like a washing machine: it is a centrifuge, a motor mainly, with its axle pointing straight up and carrying a merry-go-round for test tubes. They can be swung around in it, with their bottoms tilting away from the center, circling up to about ten thousand times per minute, and the centrifugal force this causes will make everything in the tube feel a few thousand times heavier than it is. This force will make the red blood cells, which are the heaviest component of the blood, travel most quickly toward the far, closed end of the tube. The white blood cells will follow next, and then the platelets. We must spin at least two tubes at one time, because the machine must be kept in balance. When it has spun about twenty minutes, we let it stop slowly. Then, lifting the tubes out gently, we will see a solid mass of red cells sitting packed under the pale yellow, clear liquid: the plasma. You can draw the plasma off with a syringe until the level has dropped near the red cell column's top, which is covered with a whitish film: the white cells and platelets, packed on top of the red cells.

I shall also give you a bottle of calcium chloride solution. Equal parts of the calcium chloride solution and the plasma will clot in a few minutes. There are also pipettes and other means with which to measure and transfer liquids; they are made of glass, plastics, and glass made water repellent with paraffin or silicone. Finally, a few stopwatches, and a water bath to keep anything you want at a constant temperature. Many coagulationists have worked with little more, and obtained the correct answers by asking the correct questions.

One more thing that I must say before you think on your own for a little while: there is always a strange relationship between lines written here and now (New York, September 1966) and the same ones read by you, where? when? And they are strangest when they order you around. I do not know you well, your brain may have developed more than mine, but one thought I suppose is there: that your blood is interesting, and that this book may show you why. Everything is interesting, and everything alive is endearing. I can thank fate for starting me working with blood, and now for letting me tell you about my work, but chance could have submerged me in love with anything else alive. As it is, blood is what I love studying most, and I have come to believe that it must be thought about and loved, or else it has been wasted. No blood spilled in battle or disaster could have been wasted more than the unspilled blood that dies unloved with the body that contains it. That is why I shall try to have you think ahead of what I write you sometimes, and to have you feel that but for fate you would be standing in my lab, not I. You will be right. The tests that scientists have done you could have thought of just as well, if you were granted their chance to read what had been done before. Now if you agree, and find no need to prove this to yourself, don't get that sheet of paper and don't plot plans for tests on it that you cannot carry out anyway. Instead just skip the blank space provided below for thought, and admire my own approach.

Here (Figure 5) is one scheme I could have followed; its rather simple steps are not new, and are almost identical to those that have revealed properties of blood proteins that are somehow changed by contact with glass. The steps are lettered: A is getting the blood in the decalcifying agent, B is pouring it into glass and plastic test tubes, C is centrifuging both, D is collecting the plasma (and saving the cells for other things), E is some more division. Now we have measured amounts of plasma in the glass tubes 1 and 2, and the plastic tubes 3 and 4. Step F is the addition of calcium chloride and starting a stopwatch.

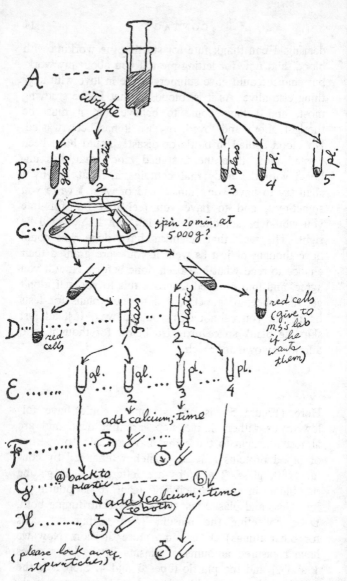

FIGURE 5

The tubes are tilted once every fifteen seconds, to see if the contents still run, and meanwhile kept in the water bath at 37 degrees Centigrade (body temperature) to make the plasma feel at home. Instead of just showing the plan as I guess I should have, I could not resist showing some results in the diagram too: tube 2 shows a shorter clotting time than tube 3. Contact with glass shortens the clotting time.

Can we find out if contact with glass had already had some effect before the calcium salt was added? Yes. We can pour some of the plasma from the glass tube (E1) into an empty plastic one (Ga), and only *then* add calcium chloride both to it and to an equal amount of plasma that never had tasted glass at all (plastic tube Gb). In the diagram, this is step H; tube Ga shows a clot in less time than tube Gb. You could say that the plasma in tube Ga is left with a glass taste. This taste fades, and you can prove that too: pour little amounts of plasma from the glass tube into a whole row of plastic tubes, add calcium chloride to one plastic tube right away, to another say five minutes later, and so on, so that the last tube of the row will have its plasma sitting around for hours between the time when it last saw glass and when it too finally receives your dose of calcium. That last tube will have such a long clotting time (counted of course from the moment you added the calcium salt!) that it obviously must have forgotten what glass was like.

Now how do we express all this scientifically? To save yourself time and impress others, replace long but clear expressions like "shortens the clotting time of," with a single long word like "activates." People who study blood clotting (coagulationists) do use that word because they feel that coagulation is an activity of some kind, and whatever brings the action faster to completion may be called an activator; the opposite is an inhibitor. So, to begin with, our statement will be: "The glass tube activated coagulation more than did the plastic tube, and this activation did not need calcium." And: "The activating effect of the glass tube disappeared in one or two hours after interruption of its contact with the plasma."

This kind of exclamation does not give scientists much satisfaction; it is only a description, not a prediction, and the distinction becomes more obvious the more accurately you describe your particular experiment.

So far, we were careful enough to write: "the glass tube . . . ," not: "a glass tube . . . ," which after only one experiment would be a rather hasty prediction. Nowadays it is more respectable to repeat any test enough times to allow the statistically supported shout: "The clotting time of normal plasma is significantly shortened by glass." Usually that means the test will work the expected way ninety-nine out of a hundred times, or better. Several controls are needed: get blood from various people, use glass powder instead of just the test tube wall, if possible change even the order of testing and let the work be done by different people and on different days, so that your conclusion and prediction need not be limited to: "On October 27, after dark and during a rainstorm approaching Chicago from the north, Aunt Emma's plasma will always clot faster in a glass tube taken from the third drawer at your right." Once the statistician is satisfied with our data, we can say: "Glass activates plasma; the activation product is unstable." Many professional articles introduce blood clotting with that statement. How little more than that is known may become clear to you later.

You may remember that I got myself into this experiment of yours by describing how I used to sit behind the microscope at night, and all I would see was the bright life of red cells drifting along, of platelets sticking and bubbling, and fibrin growing, and white cells crawling. Only, when I looked up, it was dark around me. I was in the animal house. I could hear the rabbits breathe in their cages, could see here and there the soft ghost of a body come closer to its bars, and maybe peer back at me. There was a long dusky

FIGURE 6

gap between the blood circulating nonchalantly within that live beast out there, and the coy little drop under glass that I was baby-sitting for. I saw the platelets growing sticky on the glass through the microscope. We have seen that glass also activated the plasma in your experiment. Why did glass make platelets stick and why did it activate plasma? Could it be the activation, or the activation product, whatever that was, that made the platelets stick? Or the other way around? If there was a specific activation product, should there not have been an unactive precursor, a protein maybe that was running around inside the rabbits out there, and a more dignified version of it inside me, waiting to be touched by glass (a rather unnatural desire) and be activated?

There was a very old idea that glass activates clotting because it is a wettable surface. Was wettability enough? Were blood vessel walls then water-repellent inside? And would platelets not stick to any water-repellent surface in the lab? How were these problems related to the effect of glass upon the completely unknown activation product precursor, or contact factor or intact glass factor, a factor so far without a face and name and character? Did it have to stick to glass to become activated? Could it even be the glue needed to make the platelets paste themselves to the glass?

Let me remind you that I was looking for these various answers while various other people were doing the same thing in various directions at once, and that I was not in exactly a linear race; no one is.

In those early days of my life with blood, there was not enough money available for research and for me together; part of my income had to be coaxed from the hospital by my performing routine chores for it. The Friedman test was one such routine item. It consisted of injecting urine from a human female into the earveins of a rabbit female, and killing the injected one later to see if its ovaries were red and swollen. If they were, the human female was pregnant.

It seems that it is not the cat's curiosity that always kills the cat, sadly enough, but in one way this was a helpful arrangement: it was the lady's curiosity—not mine—that killed the rabbit. For the problem I mentioned before, of only being able to look into the depths of life by tearing it open, was always a worse than philosophical one to me. I knew my rabbits. I made it a point to look deeply into the eyes of each

FIGURE 7

new arrival. Into its long, hot ears I would softly discuss the weather, so that when the time came for me to design little tests for my little theories, I would think long and hard in order to be sure there was no way but through an animal's death. And then, like all biologists I am sure, I tried to do as many quick little tests as possible in the short twilight of life remaining within the organs, like a man making light for reading a map by setting it on fire.

A simple old way of judging wettability is just by

looking at the shape of the surface that separates the air from the water placed in contact with the solid. In a wettable straw, juice halfway sucked up in it will have a hollow surface, and in a water repellent straw the surface will be more or less straight.

Blood vessels are coated inside with a thin film of cells, called endothelium. (The -thelium part is a distortion of a Greek word meaning "nipple," and I presume the whole word serves mainly to demonstrate the advantages of a classical education.) Narrow blood vessels look red because they are transparent. Where they run through transparent tissue, as in the mesentery, which is an almost glass-clear fold from which the small intestines hang, one can see the light shine through them, and under a microscope see the red cells rush by.

The mesenteric veins seemed ideal for our study. Therefore I injected some air into the mesenteric veins of several "Friedman rabbits." The blood/air interface in the vessels always seemed straight. We were delighted. The blood vessels' walls were not wettable for blood—that was news. But when the time came to publish this very simple observation, I decided to make very sure. Maybe, I thought, the opacity of the blood had hidden the hollow of the interface.

From a rabbit, I collected some blood into an anticoagulant, centrifuged it, drew the clear plasma up into a syringe with a three-way stopcock connected to its tip, and attached an air-filled syringe to the stopcock. Then, after the rabbit had been killed, I could first inject air into a mesenteric blood vessel to chase the red cells aside, then turn the stopcock and from the second syringe inject plasma into the clear air space (see Figure 8). Now I could see the plasma/air interface, and it was hollow. Then I injected oil into

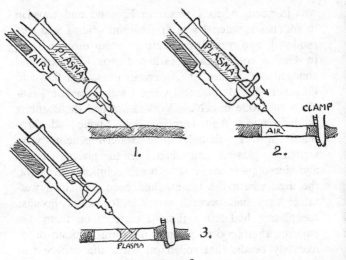

FIGURE 8

the plasma space, and the oil stayed round, telling me that it did not want to coat the endothelium, that it would rather have the plasma do that. I had seen similar behavior in glass tubes, and opposite behavior in plastic ones of certain kinds. So the endothelium was wettable, wettable for blood. Could it be, however, that some surfaces existed that were wettable for blood but not for water, and still delayed clotting because of this property alone?

I began to look at all dead surfaces in the lab, to pour blood over them, then I rinsed them off with salt solution (because plain water would rupture the cells and platelets), and I looked again. I used Lucite sheet, pieces of plastic tablecloth, paraffin blocks, and also the chromium-plated lid of an old soapbox that had belonged to my father, and that I happened to have with me when I escaped from Holland after it was invaded, when I sailed to England and traveled to Indonesia, when I was drafted and when I was surrendered, and went from camp to camp through Java, to Osaka and Nagaoka, when I was liberated and changed my clothes for American ones, was flown to Okinawa and Manila, and when I sailed for San Francisco and rode into New York. I washed the soapbox lid before use. And, surprise, both Lucite and chromium surface, though quite water-repellent, were wetted by plasma, and when I let the plasma run off and rinsed these surfaces with salt solution and water, the area where the plasma had been, remained wettable; they had become wettable for water because the plasma had left a film of material on them. On paraffin, the blood or plasma just formed round drops like tiny beads, that rolled off when the surface was tilted, and that left no wettable trace. Only when I polished the paraffin, with a piece of washed ice, for example, that would leave no mess of its own, would the paraffin behave as the Lucite and the chromium. And when I melted the paraffin surface a bit with hot water, it became blood-repellent again. As a rule, then, I could say that blood could only wet water-repellent surfaces by making them water-wettable!

The next question was: Does blood or plasma take longer to clot on these surfaces that it wets but that repel water? Longer than it takes on glass, which is wettable for both blood and water? I did clotting times until I felt sure that the answer was yes. Now only one more experiment was needed to show that the endothelium resembled Lucite and family: if I could add something to the blood and keep it from depositing its film onto the solid, the solid would be repellent for the blood. And if that something could be injected into the bloodstream without harm, the endothelium, with a little bit of luck, might still appear repellent, and the plasma/air interface prepared as before, would be straight. I found a special detergent that did all this, almost—it kept blood from wetting Lucite, it could be injected into the bloodstream of a rabbit without harm, in amounts that would keep its blood from depositing films on Lucite—but the rabbit's blood vessel walls remained wetted by its plasma.

I never published all these little tests of fifteen years ago. They seemed homely, and only a dope or a genius can afford to publish rustic and naïve-looking work—and I'm never sure which I am. My father once watched the great physicist Hendrik A. Lorentz who in turn held his coffee spoon and rinsed it for more than ten minutes to watch the water bounce off and form its twisted fan. Franklin, Langmuir, and other great physicists have published parlor tricks with explanations that advanced our knowledge to an embarrassing degree. I wish I could do that too.

I began to wonder if at least part of the films left on surfaces might contain certain coagulation factors. After all, most of these coagulation factors were presumed to be proteins, and I presumed my films to be protein too. But there are probably thousands of different protein species in the blood, and the only good way of telling them apart thus far is by the work they can do. Would my films be willing to work, even if they were only one molecule thick—and I suspected after doing some reading that they might be no thicker than that? The film left on Lucite did not seem very excited, because that dash of detergent which I could add to prevent plasma from depositing a film did not make its clotting time longer. In other words: for clotting in Lucite, film deposition was no help. Would films also be formed by contact of plasma with glass?

And would these be more active? If such films would
be as water-wettable as the glass itself was already,
how could I see them, or at least how could I see them
work? There was one job they appeared to do visibly
on both Lucite and glass: they seemed to glue platelets to both, for when I added some detergent to blood
that contained platelets, and so prevented it from
forming a film on Lucite, platelets also refused to
stick. If it was not the film itself, but the act of film
formation that made platelets stick, one might first
coat the Lucite or glass with plasma, rinse the excess
plasma off, and then expose platelet-rich blood to the
preformed film: platelets should then refuse to stick.
It just so happened that at this point Dr. Moolten,
upon seeing an opened box of glass wool in a neighboring laboratory, stopped, stared, and said to me:
"that's it; maximum surface." Then he explained to
me that he suddenly realized only certain platelets
may be able to stick to glass, and that the best way of
measuring platelet adhesiveness would be by giving
all platelets an instantaneous, simultaneous chance to
touch and stick to glass. Then only the sticky ones
would stick.

Meanwhile, with all my thinking about the stickiness of proteins and platelets, my income had grown
beyond the rent of my room. The war which had
pinned my girl down in Holland and blown me around
the world, was finally shrinking and its ghost allowed
us to meet again after seven years. We were married,
and with the help of others began to study glass wool,
a material that easily disintegrates into itching powder.
We finally decided a 1½-inch braid was best. It was
suspended from its arms in the mouth of a test tube,
moistened with salt solution (Figure 9), and warmed
to body temperature. One cubic centimeter of blood

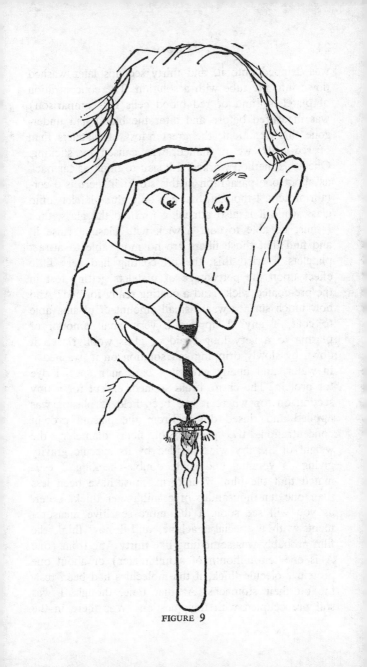

FIGURE 9

was dripped onto it, and thirty seconds later washed down into the tube with a solution. The concentration of platelets (and of red blood cells for comparison) was measured before and after the blood had undergone this treatment; the greater loss of platelets than of red cells, we presumed, was caused by sticking. Once this method worked, I began to think as far back as about one paragraph in this story: if there is a certain protein, I thought, that can only glue platelets onto glass while it is also attaching *itself* to the glass, then I must be able to coat a wick with plasma, rinse it, and find that those fibers are no more able to attract platelets. I tried this; the pre-coating had very little effect upon the percentage of platelets getting lost in the pre-coated wick. Had a coating really formed? And how much surface was a small amount of plasma able to coat, if any? I applied a very small amount of plasma to a very long braid of glass wool, rinsed it down by slowly dripping salt solution on it, washed it in water, and finally gave it a bath in a special dye for protein. The entire braid stained, except for a tiny section on top where it had been held as plasma was applied and rinsed down. From the plasma protein concentration, the glass wool fiber diameter, the weight of the dry wick divided by its specific gravity giving its volume, and some double-checking, I estimated that the film, if uniform, must have been less than one ten-thousandth of a millimeter thick. Later, as you will see soon, I did more sensitive measurements with a special machine, and I now think the film probably was something like thirty Ångström (one Å is one ten-millionth of a millimeter) or about one protein molecule thick, if the molecules had been resting on their stomachs. At that time, though, I was still preoccupied with the question: Was there in the plasma a specific ingredient that formed these films, an ingredient that was also needed to make platelets stick, while or after it had been deposited?

This was no idle question. When you cut yourself, it is not the complete clotting of blood in the wound, not the seal of fibrin, that stops you bleeding so soon, but a plug of platelets that accumulate right where the small skin vessels were cut. What makes the platelets stick there and only there? There are two diseases to show what happens if platelets stick too little or too much. If they do not stick enough, you will bleed longer, and even when you bump your skin, the slight damage to small vessels below the surface will make them bleed and show as a larger-than-normal black-and-blue mark. On the other hand, if your platelets stick too well, or find places to clump where they shouldn't, they will form plugs within blood vessels that have not been cut. Such a plug is called a white thrombus; it may block some blood upstream enough to have it form fibrin, trapping the red cells in a real clot called red thrombus. Thrombosis, especially in the vessels of the heart muscles, can cause death quickly. If I could find that mysterious glue that regulates platelet stickiness, I would be a useful organism indeed. I did not find that glue.

Chemical, and even electrical mechanisms have since been found by others; a well-known and rather simple substance, called ADP, must probably be present to make platelets adhere. It is widespread in living things; it may, for example, leak out of red blood cells when these are slightly damaged and thus make platelets sticky. Its full name is adenosine diphosphate, meaning that its body, adenosine, has a tail of two phosphate groups. If the prefix "di" would be changed to "mono" (making AMP) or to "tri" (making ATP) by respectively removing or adding a phosphate group, the molecule would become unable to make platelets adhere to things. Yet, the ADP itself is probably not the glue, but rather the key that unlocks the glue box. The very specific demand of the platelet for a key with two, and not one or three phosphate groups, suggests that the platelet membrane must have a very specific lock to be fitted.

What we need now is a patient with a wrong lock or glue. If the glue must be in the platelets, such a patient with non-sticky platelets can have normal plasma. His platelets, transferred to somebody else's plasma, would still not stick. If the glue must be in the plasma, then this hypothetical patient's platelets will become adhesive normally when placed in normal plasma, and anybody else's platelets will become non-adhesive in the patient's plasma. Perhaps we shall know soon. At this point, I feel like a child afraid to sleep through Christmas, because as I am writing this I may be missing an article published yesterday and explaining and discovering all. Meanwhile, I can only tell you a few negative discoveries, to demonstrate what patients can do, and have done, for scientists.

Hemophilia

There are people born without fibrinogen. Nothing can make their blood clot—except, of course, fibrinogen. It is true that their platelets will not stick to glass, but from superficial cuts, they do not bleed abnormally long: their platelets stick normally there. Does that mean neither fibrinogen nor fibrin is the glue we are looking for? A more popularized disease, maybe a more dramatic one, is hemophilia. Hemophiliacs do have a clotting time of often an hour or more, instead of ten to fifteen minutes; but, like patients lacking fibrinogen, they do not bleed long from small skin cuts. Is whatever they lack a platelet glue? We must return to this later (p. 105).

What do they lack? Hemophilia is an ancient disease, inherited by sons from mothers who seem healthy. The clotting times of such boys can be corrected by adding a very small amount of normal plasma, or a bit of the proteins collected from normal plasma. The strange pattern of inheritance, and the simple correction test, gave hemophilia the appearance of being one, and only one disease. Simple tests were done during World War II to prove that there is more than one hemophilia. You could have designed them yourself and can even do so now. Imagine you have four hemophiliacs, A, B, C, and D; four syringes, and about eight test tubes. What can you do?

Pretend you did this: marked the syringes according to the patients, to draw bloods A, B, C, and D, and pre-mark the test tubes the same, and the four extra ones A+B, B+C, C+D, and, for example, A+D. Let someone help you to take blood from the four patients almost simultaneously, place two cubic centimeters from each into the corresponding first four tubes, and then one cubic centimeter of blood A into tube A+B and one into tube A+D, and so on to get the proper mixtures into the correspondingly labeled tubes. Now let us pretend you found long clotting times in tubes A, B, C, D, C+D, and A+D, but short ones in tubes A+B and B+C. Since A and B corrected each other, they cannot have lacked the same thing. B and C also differed, but C and D, D and A, and therefore C and A were all suffering from the same abnormality. It just so happens that the two hemophilias discovered were actually called hemophilia A and B, so that in rather modern language we may have found that your patient B had hemophilia B and patients A, C, and D had hemophilia A. Sadly enough, during the war when these actual experiments were done, contact among scientists was poor. In England, a boy named Christmas was the first one found with hemophilia B, and the disease was called Christmas disease; it was also presumed he lacked a factor present in normal blood, and this was called Christmas factor. This was of course an abbreviation of "Everyoneelse'sbutlittleboychristmas's" factor.

Meanwhile, in the United States, a new form of hemophilia was discovered, presumably caused by a deficiency of a coagulation factor called Plasma Thromboplastin Component (PTC for short). It took many letters flying across the Atlantic with plasma samples enclosed, before it was agreed that PTC = Christmas factor; lacking in hemophilia B = Christmas disease. Others found that the factor is not really absent but merely abnormal, and that even normally it is not an isolated protein but part of the prothrombin molecule that comes off during clotting and acquires a more or less specific activity. They labeled it Autoprothrombin II. Obviously, a court of arbitration was needed to declare a truth if truth could not be found any other way. And indeed, a group of coagulationists, now meeting yearly, decided the activity known as "PTC, etc." was now Factor IX, and the activity lacking in the "real" hemophiliac's blood, previously known as Anti Hemophilic Globulin (AHG) and by at least three other names, was now to be called Factor VIII. The numerals are from a rather German proposal, that goes as far as calling calcium Factor IV, a rather odd name for an element. To be consistent, one should call wettable surfaces Factor 0, since the numbers were given in order of discovery, and wettable surfaces were probably already known to prehistoric shrimps.

Which one of all these turned out to be the contact factor? Plasma lacking in prothrombin, fibrinogen, calcium, Factors VIII and IX, but having been shaken with glass powder, can still shorten the clotting time of normal plasma kept in plastic. That indicates that the contact factor is none of the ones we mentioned so far.

In 1953, Drs. R. L. Rosenthal, O. H. Dreskin, and N. Rosenthal at Mount Sinai Hospital in New York City published an article entitled: "New hemophilia-like disease caused by deficiency of a third plasma thromboplastin factor" (in *Proceedings of the Society for Experimental Biology and Medicine,* Vol. 82, p. 171). Their patients, one uncle and his two nieces, bled just a little too much after tooth extractions, and turned out to have clotting times of fifteen to twenty-nine minutes. A more sensitive test, that measures the rate of prothrombin conversion to thrombin, was more definitely abnormal. The abnormal clotting could be corrected with normal plasma, or with plasma from patients lacking Factor VIII or IX: a new hemophilia was discovered. Factor X, which I will not discuss here, had already been found, so that the "new" factor presumed lacking in these three patients was eventually granted the name XI.

Two years after this discovery, guess where I was lucky enough to be given a job, and guess where I could now enjoy the extreme luxury of finding some Factor XI-deficient plasma at any time of night by just opening a tremendous freezer and carefully reading a label? At Mount Sinai Hospital, I began to spend evenings working for my thesis, to get a rather belated Ph.D. degree in Holland. Surface contact was still my hobby, and I pursued it now in a beautiful, stainless steel and polished stone world, under a bitingly bright light, in silence.

On one of the first nights, Factor XI-deficient plasma shaken with glass showed itself unable to shorten the clotting time of normal plasma kept in plastic. I decided that I had made a great discovery: Factor XI was needed for glass activation. Then I decided to expand an old trick I had tried in New Brunswick before Factor XI was known: I poured plasmas with various deficiencies each into glass tubes and out, rinsed the tubes out, centrifuged them upside down to dry, placed measured small amounts of the various plasmas into the variously coated tubes to produce all kinds of combinations between type of coating and type of plasma added, then added calcium to all, and started my stopwatch. As I had desired, I found that the nicest shortening of clotting time was given by coatings of normal plasma to the samples of Factor XI-deficient plasma placed in the tube. So the glass had adsorbed Factor XI from the normal plasma and, I presumed happily, had been activated at the surface; the activated Factor XI then must have reacted with something in the Factor XI-deficient plasma as it would in normal plasma.

I think it was only a few days later that Dr. O. D. Ratnoff and Joan E. Colopy, in Cleveland, Ohio, published an article entitled: "A familial hemorrhagic trait associated with a deficiency of a clot-promoting fraction of plasma" (*Journal of Clinical Investigation*, Vol. 34, p. 602, 1955). It seemed that there was this

Mr. I. J. R. Hageman, a rather healthy thirty-seven-year-old railroad brakeman, who needed a small operation. As a routine precaution, his clotting time was taken; it turned out to be eighty-seven minutes, so long that his blood could be centrifuged without first receiving an anticoagulant. When the cell-poor plasma was then collected, it often did not clot at all. Addition of a little normal, or VIII-, IX-, or XI-deficient plasma, brought the clotting time down to normal. Thus, Mr. Hageman, who was not even a bleeder, became the proud owner of a newly discovered deficiency: the lack of Hageman factor, or, after nomination and confrontation with the now anxiously counting Nominating Committee, Mr. Hageman could announce with official approval that he lacked Factor XII. Worse yet: it soon became apparent to the Cleveland group that Mr. Hageman's plasma, shaken with glass, was utterly unable to shorten the clotting time of normal plasma that had not been in contact with glass. Factor XII, in short, must be the contact factor.

I felt this was a great discovery, made by two very nice people who knew quite well what they were doing but who also were quite lucky; or, to describe my feelings more precisely, I was quite peeved. Here I had been sitting in the silent castle where Factor XI had been born, I had nursed it to become the Prince of Contact, and now a foreigner to my thesis was to be King. As soon as I recovered, I began to want a patient like Mr. Hageman. Since, apparently, Mr. Hageman had no symptoms of bleeding at all, and was discovered completely by accident, I merely had to wait until I took the right person's clotting time by mistake.

About three weeks before I had to round off my thesis work, one of the staff physicians, already well

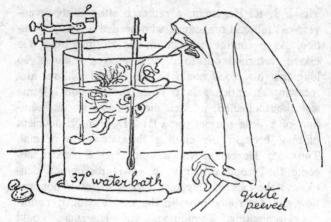

37° waterbath

quite peeved

FIGURE 10

known as a scientist and even more as The One Perfect Gentleman, walked into the lab and said: "Leo, I think I have a patient who may interest you." A few days later, a tall and apparently perfectly healthy patient came in, rolled up his sleeve, and donated about thirty cc of Factor XII-deficient blood. When I said, "Press on the cotton, please," he asked: "Are you sure you got enough?" I said, "Yes, I think so," and he said, "That's good, because I am not going to give another drop of blood to anybody from now on." He has kept his word so far, left town a few years ago heading south, and in the seven years since that moment when I had said I had gotten enough, only one other person lacking Factor XII has been found in New York City. Meanwhile, in those few weeks, I could only confirm the Cleveland results: Factor XII (but also my own Factor XI) was needed for activation by glass.

Later, others found that actually Factor XII is the

one that must go onto the glass first, where it becomes activated. It will then attract Factor XI, they say. The resulting activated Factor XI or maybe some Factors XI–XII complex, is called "activation product." People who are prone to forming thrombi may have this product circulating in their blood, because their clotting time in plastic is sometimes as short as it is in glass. Platelets were recently found to have the product on their surface. "Ha!" you shriek, "this is the Glue!" Perhaps it is; you know as much about it as I do, and I am not studying platelets in my lab these days. What I am doing is a very pleasant result of some other work I started at Mount Sinai Hospital. It demands a very close look at proteins in general, and I have begun to look at them so closely that any aspect of life too far away to see its very molecules at work, looks faceless and dead to me.

II

HOW WE PLAY WITH PROTEINS

I think I know what still bothers me about the word "protein." I always hated the taste of cooked fish, and the first symbol for protein I must have faced at the sensitive age of seven, was a lifelessly drawn dead mackerel reclining within its section of a badly drawn circle, plus an indication of how much of me was it. Then, about ten years later, the proteins came back to me, this time to be cooked in chemistry experiments that were as dead as the original fish. And after fifteen more years, working in New Brunswick, I could see in the blood chemistry lab next door how proteins were mostly a hindrance; to measure various substances, a blood sample first had to be mixed with an acid that turned the proteins into a curdled chocolate pudding, utterly inedible.

Much work with proteins seemed to lead away from their individual beauty, and toward amorphous statistical and unemotional values. No normal person will rush away to a far land upon hearing it produces 9.3 billion kattis of rice; it will help to hear that many of its producers have long eyelashes and perfect lips. And if he has to go there anyway, on business, it will be his interest in eyelashes that makes the trip a success. And so, my business being blood clotting and platelets, I prepared for a trip deeper into proteinland by buying myself some new and good-looking and -smelling books about proteins, and started to read.

A bad start. To be as deep as it is fat, a scientific book nowadays must be written by an entire group of people, and one among them will be a bum who hands in his chapter one or two years late, when all the other chapters have become obsolete. Therefore, you cannot tell the freshness of a textbook from the date it was published; you must look at the dates of other publications it refers to inside the text. Books on proteins should contain at least some references to articles less than one year old. (This little book is no textbook, so it does not have to contain any references like that.)

Luckily, I then began to read chemical journals as well. Already alarmed by novelties in the books, I now became panicked by the constant stream of strangeness pouring over my head from fresher sources: I realized that I must learn more about the structure of the atom.

The Atom

I had forgotten all about the atom since before World War II; now, being stared in the face by obvious references to protons and electrons, I had to relearn. I don't think I have to know all the new particles that have been found in the nucleus, but it is good to remember the protons in it, each providing a unit of positive electric charge. And remember the electrons: they are the units of negative charge that spin around the nucleus. The orbits they follow have very fixed shapes and sizes with space in each for one pair of electrons, one electron spinning one way, the other the opposite way. Sets of orbitals form shells. They are indicated with the letters K (inner shell, containing the single orbital called 1s), L (the shell around K; contains one orbital called 2s, and three orbitals called 2p), M (with its one 3s, three 3p, and five 3d orbitals), and that is as far as I want to go. The next thing to remember is that nature dislikes explosive situations. If something is unbalanced and contains what you could call an unsatisfied urge, nature tries to satisfy it as soon and as simply as possible.

But even with the single atom, there is usually a dissatisfied and unsatisfiable condition. It wants two things that its size may forbid it to have at the same time: one is to be electrically neutral (have as many electrons spinning around as it has protons in its nucleus), the other is to have its shells entirely and exactly occupied with electrons. As you can see from this table, helium, neon, and argon (He, Ne, and Ar)

	$1s$	$2s$	$2p$	$3s$	$3p$
1 H	1				
2 He	2				
3 Li	2	1			
4 Be	2	2			
5 B	2	2	1		
6 C	2	2	2		
7 N	2	2	3		
8 O	2	2	4		
9 F	2	2	5		
10 Ne	2	2	6		
11 Na	2	2	6	1	
12 Mg	2	2	6	2	
13 Al	2	2	6	2	1
14 Si	2	2	6	2	2
15 P	2	2	6	2	3
16 S	2	2	6	2	4
17 Cl	2	2	6	2	5
18 Ar	2	2	6	2	6

are neutral when their shells are full at the same time. That is what makes them noble gases: they need no electrons, they give no electrons, they do not easily react with any other atoms, they are completely satisfied. For the other small atoms the world contains more adventures. If they want to complete their shells by themselves, they will lose their electrical balance: the full L shell must contain eight (four pairs) of electrons, which would give oxygen two extra negative charges, for example; and sodium (Na), if it dropped its lonely electron in the M shell, would wander around with two neatly filled shells (K and L) but with a net positive charge. Such charged atoms (or charged chemical combinations of atoms) are called negative or positive ions. The hydrogen ion is a hydrogen atom that has lost its one and only electron, so we can call its remainder just a naked proton. It can form a bridge between two negative atoms: a hydrogen bond.

The Hydrogen Bond

The hydrogen bond is not a chemical bond: it forms and snaps again too easily. However, if let us say one atom of F meets one atom of Na, a combination is formed—as you can see from the table—that can have full shells and be electrically balanced at the same time, as if it were some kind of new noble element: the Na and F have formed a chemical compound, NaF, by sharing electrons. Anyone who has been a child will tell you that perfect sharing, fifty-fifty, does not exist. Atoms too have such problems, and often one atom gets a greater half than the other; probably, a substance that is equally stable when ionized will not share electrons between its atoms all the time but will let atoms or atom groups form its own full shells and act as more or less independent charged particles part of the time. Of course, negative and positive ions will attract each other, so complete freedom does not exist, even for ions floating around in water.

Water itself is not as simple as it sounds or looks. It is called H_2O in junior high school, and college may still draw it as H-O-H, but at a four-day conference on the structure of water, specialists could not agree how it actually is. They did agree that hydrogen bonds form between H atoms of one water molecule and O atoms of two other water molecules, a bit like Y-shaped magnets. You can imagine how many arrangements you can make with a few dozen of those. Some will be as regular as crystals, and such shapes may exist not only in ice and snow, but also around small foreign molecules; others will be more random, lumpy and snaky things; all will be hollow (Figure 11).

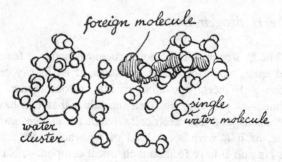

FIGURE 11

Hydrophobic Bonding

Still, you must not think that water molecules prefer each other to anything else. Only when their hydrogen bonds have nothing else to hold on to, will they hold the molecules of water structured. For example, a hydrophobic (water-repelling, nonwettable) molecule such as a chain of carbon atoms saturated with hydrogen atoms, forms no hydrogen bonds, and if forced into water, big as it is, it will destroy whatever structure of water existed before, and the broken hydrogen bonds will mend to leave a minimal number freely facing this unfriendly foreign thing. On the other hand, molecules, that contain available sites for

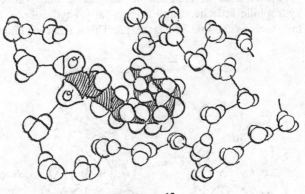

FIGURE 12

hydrogen bonding, such as salts, or NH_2 groups or oxygen, will be glad to mix with water, and the water molecules, sharing hydrogen bonds with these friendly, hydrophilic, wettable things will form rather stable units with them. Now remember that nature tries to satisfy as soon and as simply as possible, and you can predict what will happen if we put two hydrophobic molecules in water at the same time. The simplest way to avoid contact with water is for the two to hold on to each other; it reduces their surface and reduces the amount of work that the water around them has to do arranging itself. Such sticking together of hydrophobic molecules in water is called hydrophobic bonding. Hydrophobic bonds can also form between the fattier parts of one or more molecules and affect their shapes in solution. Thrown into oil, there would be no need for them to keep their water-repellent surfaces stuck together, and no hydrophobic bonds have to form; hydrogen bonds are then stronger.

A nice kind of molecule to imagine is one with a hydrophilic little head and a long, fatty (hydrophobic) tail, such as the one in Figure 13. Think what a bunch

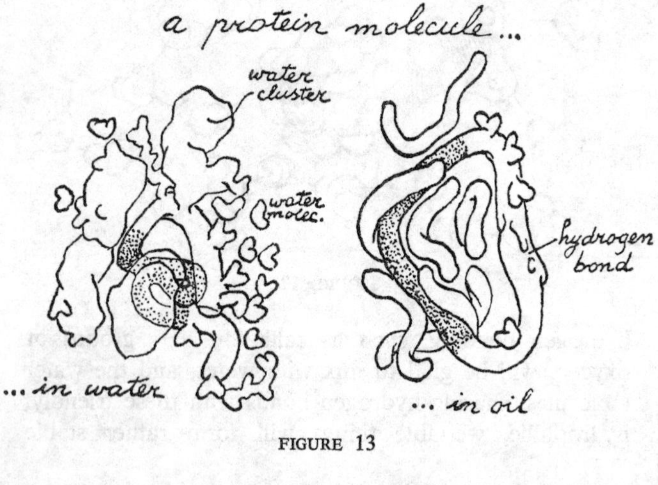

a protein molecule...

water cluster

water molec.

hydrogen bond

...in water

...in oil

FIGURE 13

of these would do, how they would arrange themselves, in water, and in oil, and in a mixture of water and oil; that is how detergents and emulsifiers arrange themselves. Your blood contains many of them.

Now we have talked about forces that hold molecules together, and shape them; the same ones that also tell them how to live among other molecules as relaxed as possible: the tight, chemical bonds needed to fill electron shells among the atoms, the more bouncy electrostatic ties between positive and negative ions, the hydrogen bonds, actually being just little protons holding two negative atoms wherever the occasion wants them, and finally the hydrophobic bonds, weaker than the others, actually a side effect of hydrogen bond formation among the water molecules around them.

It may be good to realize that from all this, the shape of the molecule appears like a cloud in the mist. If we were their size, and electrons were white, we would move among stiff-spined and soft-spined bunches of bubbles of fog, and some would be in very rapidly forming and fragmenting, fleeting cages of fog: water. The softness is a statistical one, like the softness of a fast-spinning fan that we can describe as a thick translucent disk made of about 50 per cent metal and 50 per cent air: true and false. If you stick your finger in it, half the time it will hit air, and though the other half seems more important it is actually the change that counts. The molecule too is shrouded in what seems a shape and is actually a complex of events: the spinning and oscillating of electrons within and among all the outer shells of all its atoms; their heavy, positive nuclei remain hidden more the heavier they are. And now, back to proteins.

Protein Formation

C, N, O, and H are the small and variably active
atoms that make up most of the protein body.
Stretched out, against its will, it would be a long body,
and as complex in shape and meaning as a long, hand-
written word. A chain, and every link a choice among
twenty possible shapes of links. Each link is called an
amino acid, and the sketch below, better than human
words, shows you how together the amino acids can
spell an infinite number of words. The connections
between the amino acids are made, as you can see,
by the OH of a —COOH group and the H of an —NH$_2$
group falling off to form a molecule of H$_2$O. Now
you can run along from one amino acid to the
next, as you can along a written word like the "tile,"

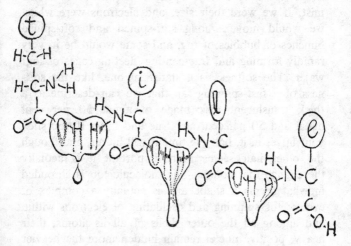

FIGURE 14

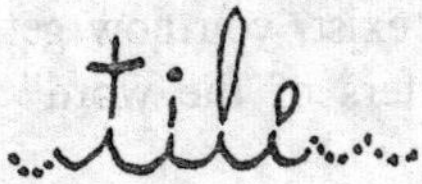

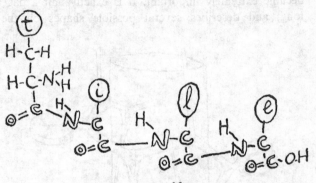

FIGURE 15

below. Similarly, the backbone of a protein molecule
is made up of all the sections of amino acid that go:
−N−C−C−O. If you put a few amino acids together
this way, you are only building such a small protein

FIGURE 16

that it is not even called a protein, but a peptide (di-
peptide, tripeptide, etc.) or at most a polypeptide, but
the angles they are connected with must even give
small peptides peculiar shapes.

Sizes and angles of the backbone bonds have been
measured and calculated. For example, the O− on
the one C and the H on the N next to it are pointing
in exactly opposite directions, so that they all lie in
one plane, but the −C− that would be to the left of
the N on this diagram will hold the remainder of the
amino acid out at some angle. Since this remainder,
called amino acid residue, is the part in which the

twenty variations exist, you now get the picture of zig-zag with the "letters of the word" sticking out in all directions.

In reality, the backbone itself is very often coiled, completely or only over certain sections forming a very regular helix, as if wound around an invisible, no an absent rod. Such a helix was first described by Linus Pauling and Robert B. Corey in a communication (*J. Am. Chem. Soc.,* Vol. 72, p. 5349, 1950) that became extremely important. It is exactly half a page long, and describes several possible shapes on the

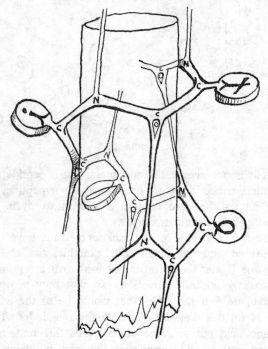

FIGURE 17

basis of bond angles and sizes; the helix is the most elegant. It appears that, if you do imagine winding a polypeptide chain around a stick of the proper thickness, CO and NH groups will point exactly at each other as shown below, and form hydrogen bonds that hold the helix together, as you can see in Figure 17. However, there are several amino acids that do not fit in this helix; wherever they occur, they will be like a bend in an old metal spring, but again a bend of a definite angle. So what do we have now, instead of a straight written word? We have it first with the letters sticking at odd angles out of the paper, then the paper strip wound around a stick, and then the stick broken at definite places (Figure 18).

FIGURE 18

All these contortions appear caused by chemical bonds, and hydrogen bonds. Where do hydrophobic bonds come in? Many of the twenty amino acids that a protein can use are more or less hydrophobic. Quite a few residues have straight, round, or branched fatty tails. If the protein backbone on which they sit is not too stiff, and it is thrown into water, the hydrophobic amino acids, unable to tear themselves off, will force the backbone to which they are chemically stuck into weird bends in their effort to clump their hydrophobic bodies together. Often they are presumed successful, and manage to hold onto each other with hydrophobic bonds, hiding away from the water by occupying the heart of the balled-up spring.

I think we can go quite a bit farther by calling protein molecules words—or at least running-on sentences. For example, we can say that the meaning of the sentence-like molecule, its function, is what it says, and if it is normally coiled up, with parts of it hidden, then either its function is normally hidden, or else it has to be read not by following its helix around and around, but straight down the axis (the nonexisting stick). In that case, breaking its hydrogen bonds and hydrophobic bonds, as is necessary for the analysis of its amino acid sequence, and unwinding it, may put the letters neatly in a row, but their message will then be destroyed. It may then read: MENU FOR DADS BEERR (without the spacing), while if properly helixed, the letters numbered 1, 4, 7, 10, 13, and 16 will all land exactly under each other. Or the sentence may form loops normally, aligning letters 1, 2, 3, 10, and 11, and 6, 7, 8, 14, and 15, in a kind of random coil.

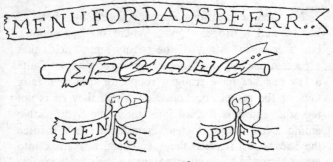

FIGURE 19

You will find many examples of the mysterious appearance or disappearance of protein activities in the blood plasma, that will probably be explained in the future on this basis. Enzymes, for example, are proteins that in very small amounts can speed up chemical reactions about a million times, and they are very specific: there are various dehydrogenases, that remove hydrogen atoms from specific spots of specific molecule types, and proteases, that split proteins (sometimes including their own bodies!) only at specific amino acids, and many of these enzymes are, must be, normally inactive while circulating in your blood. If there is any coherent story in the relationship between all these coiled-up words, maybe it can only be understood if one is aware of all meanings shown across and inside and along each word and sentence at the same time.

The beauty of plasma, very much like that of language, is then in its context, and in the way all words limit one another to give their combination a meaning greater than their sum. If that is true, then all our experiments with single proteins are like those experiments that a child performs with the words of its parent: "Watch out, that flame is hot." "Hot?" says the child and pokes its finger in the flame. "Don't sit on Mommy's lap. Mommy is too hot." "Hot?" Poke. It notes there is hot and hot. When it learns to read, it will note that the "hot" in "shot" is not hot. It may be amazed to find that "shot" and "hotel" have "hot" in common. Protein chemists have the same problem. We are not sure how much the function of any specific sequence of amino acid residues will be affected by the neighboring ones. We are only starting to synthesize chains of amino acids and observing their behavior. This is like writing random series of letters and then observing your mother's face when she tries to read them. The other approach still is: listening to mother Nature and trying to unravel the meaning of each sequence in each context. In either case, we must have some way of lifting out whole, intact words for reference: we must separate proteins alive and prove that we are doing just that.

Protein Analysis

The crudest measure to tell one protein molecule from another by, is its weight. It depends on the number of amino acid residues it contains, and on their size. In principle, the molecular weight is easily found: put the protein in a liquid of known specific gravity and see how well it sinks. The gravity of earth is not strong enough to make the single molecules sink straight and fast enough; we must centrifuge the solution to force them down, and they demand a force created by spinning their solution at about forty thousand revolutions per minute or more. While you can spin blood cells down at a tenth of that speed, you need a centrifuge that is just about ten times bigger to create enough force for molecules; the ultracentrifuge takes half a living room to rotate a thimbleful of liquid. The machine has an optical system to show where the solution becomes densest—that is the level at which the molecules of protein have become most concentrated. If they assemble at two or more levels in the tube at the same time, there is more than one kind of large molecule present.

The size of protein molecules is sometimes measured by the way they scatter light, by the volume they occupy in solution, or the surface they occupy in a

ultracentrifuge
(for molecules)

Tabletop centrifuge
(for larger particles)

FIGURE 20

film; but all results depend on the molecules' unknown shape, some only revealing their length or width or a complex relation between the two. You can also buy a kind of gel-forming plastic stuff that actually consists of tiny balls with very uniform pores in them; you can order the pores to be of a size just a bit smaller or larger than you think the protein molecules are which you want to separate. This way, you can let the porous balls suck out of your unclean mixture all molecules that are smaller than the protein you want, and after that, the protein itself.

You can also make your protein stick to the surface of things. Such sticking is called adsorption. (Sticking inside things is called *ab*sorption). I think you can take just about any solid that does not dissolve in your solution of proteins. If its surface is not uniform, it will have extra electrons in certain spots, lack of them in others. The least rigid protein molecule in a mixed solution will then be the first to stick with its own charged spots of excess and shortage of electrons, onto such a surface. Then, other and maybe more rigid protein molecules will still find some bare spots to stick to with some of their oppositely charged tips. On the other hand, if the surface is made of molecules that do not even hold on to each other very well, or onto hydrogen bond-hungry matter like water —in other words if the solid is rather soft and hydrophobic—the least rigid protein coming in contact with it may be happy to open its fatty heart toward such a surface, and stick to it with hydrophobic bonds. On any surface, you may expect a sequence of adsorption, a parade of adhesions.

The separation of proteins and other molecules is beautifully demonstrated in a very popular way called chromatography. In principle, it is just this: you shape a large amount of surface into a non-dissolving kind of thing, apply a bit of your mixed solution in one spot of the thing, and then allow a lot of pure liquid to be sucked up by the thing, past the spot of application. You may have done this yourself often by accident. If you spill ink on a piece of material, and then try to remove it by applying water to the center of the blotch, you may see the color spread out and form a ring; and if you are lucky enough to have spilled a mixture of colors, the ring is likely to grow into a circular rainbow: the different dyes will have been dragged along by the spreading water, but they were hindered to different degrees by their own specific charge distributions and their shapes in relation to those of the material and the water. Each dye is thus hindered differently and falls behind the front of water creeping ahead, each dye forming its own, slower front. In actual chromatography, filter paper is most popular, and to separate large amounts, a larger volume of your mixture can be washed down a whole stack of filter paper disks, and then split where you want. Very complex mixtures, like the host of pieces left after an enzyme has partially digested a protein, are often hard to separate with just one solvent. It may contain, for example, three peptides that are all dragged along by water at the same speed, though that speed differs from all others. Had the three peptides been dragged by some kind of alcohol, they would have traveled at different speeds from each other, but at the same speed as some other peptide also present. What would you do? A nice solution is shown in Figure 21. It is called two-dimensional paper chromatog-

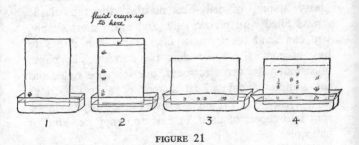

fluid creeps up to here

FIGURE 21

raphy, and digested proteins form such an intricate and specific pattern that way that the effect has been called fingerprinting. The fingerprints do not show up until a peptide stain has been sprayed upon the dried paper. As you will see later, the fingerprints of two proteins, differing only in one amino acid residue, but broken up in identical ways, will be different.

When enough purified protein must be collected to work with, chromatography is often done through a glass tube that is filled with powder (glass, resin, cellulose, any pure insoluble powder you can think of). You pour a bit of your mixture on top, and wash it slowly down with clean solvent; one, in this case invisible, ring of protein species will travel down and out into test tubes after another. You must keep testing what you collect, looking for the protein of your choice. Especially because betting on the winning protein is about as safe as betting on a horse: the speed of each depends on too many things.

Another technique, called electrophoresis, is the separation of molecules that differ in electric charge, by placing their mixture in an electric field. Molecules with the highest net charge will migrate fastest to the oppositely charged electrode. Again, you can pull the molecules through all kinds of material: slabs of glassy starch, of jelly-like plastics, through plastic straws filled with plastic jelly, and again most simply, you can send them across filter paper—but it has to be wet and salty to conduct the current. The paper must touch the two electrodes, one left, one right, and the sample is painted as a spot or a small stripe: + | − . If all goes well, the stripe will be split into copies of itself, at best one copy per kind of molecule: + ‖ | | −.

But all never goes well with plasma. It contains so many proteins that it would demand an impossibly sharp image to reveal all its components. Luckily, and as far as I am concerned, surprisingly, the net charges of them seem to fall in groups, so that the electrophoretic pattern of plasma shows several bands even with the rather blurred picture that paper gives. In this way, the separation of albumin (proteins that can dissolve in pure water) from globulin (proteins that need some salt in the water before they dissolve in it), and of globulin into alpha, beta, and gamma, and of alpha into alpha-one and alpha-two, and of beta into beta-one and beta-two, has become a routine pro-

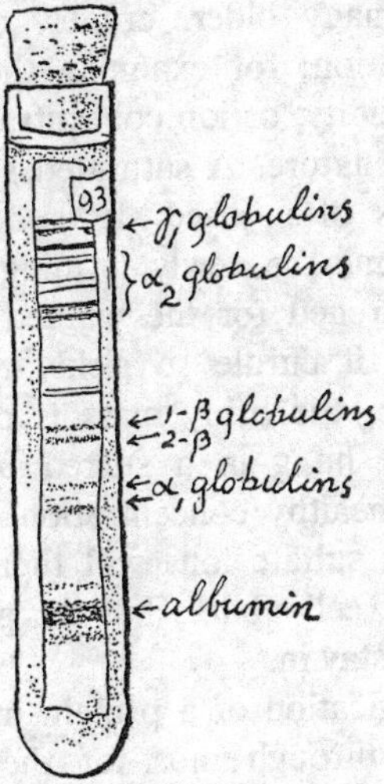

FIGURE 22

An electric field has pushed proteins out of the serum (applied at one end) at different speeds through this soft rod of plastic gel. After being stained, it is preserved in liquid. This is a rather exact copy of an actual sample. Note that the proteins in this substance do not travel in alphabetical order.

cedure in hospitals. Still, the total net charge that allows these separations is no more revealing and descriptive than your body temperature or skin color. It is the distribution and location that counts, if you want to become more personal. And again, if you want to know where the proteins went on your paper, you have to stain the paper first, and staining kills the proteins. Therefore, patterns from which the proteins must be collected alive are first split lengthwise, and one part is stained as a guide by which you can cut out and collect live samples from the unstained mate.

There are many older, cruder, duller, but useful ways of separation; for example, those based on the temperature, acidity, or ion concentration at which certain proteins denature. A saturated solution of ammonium sulfate is often used. It is added slowly, and from time to time the newly forming precipitate is removed and searched for the wanted protein. But the salt that made it curdle so sickly must be removed first by dialysis: the briny mass is placed in a cellophane bag and hung in a stirred bath containing a low and more healthy concentration of salt; the small ammonium and sulfate ions will then flow out of the bag through the cellophane, but the protein molecules, being too large, stay in.

Usually, purification of a protein in a real biochemistry lab goes through most of the techniques that you just saw, and the instructions are sometimes frightening: "precipitate with half-saturated ammonium sulfate, centrifuge, redissolve, reprecipitate, redissolve, adsorb with barium sulfate, wash powder eight times, elute with sodium citrate, dialyze, chromatograph on DEAE, find fraction with highest activity, run starch block electrophoresis, activity is in second band to right of application," with a lot of details added, of course. And the final blow will read something like: "must appear as a single component in ultracentrifuge; molecular weight must be about 42,000; N terminal amino acid must be glycine, C terminal must be alanine." And such a description is still as complete as a description of a sentence in terms of its first word, last word, and length. If the protein is an enzyme, its function can at least be part of its definition, along with every step in its purification: "Ping-Pongase, a protein that dissolves Ping-Pong balls, is precipitated by half-saturated, etc., adsorbed by barium sulfate, etc., terminal amino acids, etc." But complete amino acid analysis, without showing the correct sequence and space orientation of all its links, cannot give meaning to its chemistry.

There is one image that a protein can cast, almost as sharp and personal as your own shadow. It is called the absorption spectrum, and shows you how large a part of light of any wavelength does not pass through the protein solution. A good spectrophotometer will record this for you. It will have ways to send light, all the way from the slow, long, invisible infrared waves, through the visible spectrum, all the way out into the short, high-frequency, invisible ultraviolet; the light will go through two tubes of water, for example, one containing your protein, and the amounts of light coming through the two will be compared for one frequency after the other, and a curve will be drawn by a pen that moves up and down with per cent light absorbed, and across with wavelength (or frequency) to match. Why is this curve so typical? All atoms in all molecules vibrate to some degree. I asked you before to see a water molecule as a V-shaped magnet. Now you must also imagine the magnet to be made of springy stuff, with the two hydrogen atoms vibrating to and from each other, and to and from the oxygen atom. If you now think of all atoms in a protein molecule being connected with springs and even subjected to rather springy forces of other molecules, and think of the whole thing as a floating, tremendous, humming mobile with the pitch of each hummm depending on the way each bond has been built, you can imagine the deafening mixture—not a very good image. Actually, you want an image that seems to explain why this complexly vibrating thing is absorbing, not emitting light. Well then. When I was a little boy, I loved our piano and I hated playing it. One of the few really good things I could do with it was to undamp its strings with the pedal, meanwhile open the top lid, stick my head inside, and shout. All through its eternal dark-

FIGURE 23

ness, I could then hear the echo of my colorless yell breaking into a brilliant spectrum of pure notes, as each string vibrated in resonance with its own pitch that it had recognized in the mixture of my voice. The energy it needed for this resonance could have come only from one source: my own sound. It must have absorbed that particular bit of energy. Without being exactly like a piano, a molecule does absorb out of white, or other mixed light, those frequencies that its elements (the "strings") can "resonate" with. What

passes through and is recorded by the spectrophotometer pen, is that same white light minus the frequencies
that the solution has absorbed. So the absorption
spectrum must certainly be typical; as typical as the
shadow of a complete stranger. It tells you nothing
about the man, even though you can give it a name,
and recognize it if ever it returns.

Enzymes can be poisoned by other molecules. If
the poisoning molecule is much smaller than the enzyme, it must only be able to do that much damage
by attacking a vital spot in the enzyme molecule. That
being the case, it is fun to make a poison molecule
and for one of its atoms use a radioactive one. Then
you expose your enzyme to it, and immediately the
poison molecule—including its radioactive atom—goes
to the vital, active spot of the enzyme. Now you break
up the enzyme into peptides and separate those, say
by chromatography on paper. Then, you press the
paper against a photographic plate and keep it in the
dark for several days. Take it out, and you find one
spot on the plate blackened; it corresponds to one
peptide on the paper—the radioactive peptide. That
must then be the vital peptide, from which the poison
molecule is broadcasting still. Keep chopping, and you
will find the amino acid sequence on and around the
active enzyme site. You must not be shocked if you
find three or four radioactive spots, and after a year
of work must conclude that they all have the same
composition and amino acid sequence. What probably
has happened, and has been found to happen, is this:
the peptide, once chopped off, has some freedom to
stretch or curl up in different ways, especially if it
contains amino acids that have more than one atom
group able to fit in the backbone. Once such a peptide
is released from the control of the great protein body,

it can fulfill its own old dreams of what its own back-bone could look like, and it will twist away like the chopped-off piece of a worm.

Finally, an extremely elegant, difficult, and so far rewarding study has been that of pictures created by X-rays as they were scattered by the electrons of a very pure protein, especially of hemoglobin. The technique is too complex for me to describe here, or anywhere else, and certainly too submerged in mathematics for me to understand. I hope you will read the articles in *Scientific American* about it. Anyway, the hemoglobin molecule turned out indeed to have about all the features that such a protein was hoped to have. It was a coiled thing, with pieces of helix bent exactly at amino acids that should bend a helix, and with the most hydrophobic amino acids pointing inward, away from the outside world. The molecule has a known functional spot that is not protein-like, and that sticks out like a thick reddish disk protruding from the deep fatty guts of the molecule. Why like that? And the molecule changes shape a little when it takes up or releases oxygen, as if breathing it. Why? Does that help it? And another thing: the molecule functions surprisingly well when hydrophilic amino acids are replaced by other hydrophilic ones, or when hydrophobic ones are replaced by hydrophobic ones. Just don't replace a hydrophilic by a hydrophobic amino acid, or make any replacement that will change the over-all shape of the molecule: a patient who has inherited that kind of change is sick, his hemoglobin will behave in a very abnormal way. It looks as if shape and function go very much together, as if you could just as well make the whole thing out of some other polymer, like some kind of plastic; as long as its shape is like the backbone of hemoglobin, you may be able to stick that functional disk in it, see it slip automatically into the right spot, and presto, you have made artificial hemoglobin. As a matter of fact, there is such an example in nature: myoglobin, a protein shaped like hemoglobin but made out of different amino acids.

While I am writing this, I have the nagging feeling that I must add the following: here and there among lower animals you can find species—a kind of worm that lives in mud, for example—that have learned to make hemoglobin. Maybe it is a "natural" thing to make or for the laws of chance mutation and rigid heredity to drift into; maybe the survival value of such a molecule is so high to its host that it protects him against all odds, and he survives where none of his enemies can.

We can just about begin to wonder how meaning and history of the hemoglobin molecule are intertwined with its shape, because only now have its details become revealed, but we have no idea which other protein structures within us mean how much and why. Are all their shapes essential? How about the Hageman factor, the protein that seemed essential to start clotting of blood in a test tube? Many healthy people must be living without this enzyme, unaware of what they are missing, if anything. Is it then a useless relic to us others? Just as its detection is based on some useless artifact: the effect of glass? How much of each elegantly curlicued enzyme is essential, if its vital spot is so small? Is hemoglobin an exception? Could two-thirds or so of our body be useless decoration, old bulky lace we drag around like memories of the past millions of years? The more we discover about proteins, the more we discover how they can fool us. The next chapter is about normal proteins playing with us in the lab, and about some abnormal ones that play with the living bodies they inhabit.

III

HOW PROTEINS PLAY WITH US

When the Hageman factor was purified out of an original 1270 ml of plasma that Dr. Ratnoff, the discoverer, collected, and more and more inactive material had been removed, only two milligrams of active protein remained. Reconstituted, it was only as active as 165 milliliters of plasma would have been. This tells you that only 165:1270—a fraction of one-eighth of the original factor—had been recovered. It also tells you that, considering that you contain about 45 ml plasma per kilogram body weight, and you look as if you weigh about 50 kg, you must contain about $(45:165) \times 50 \times 2 =$ about 25 mg Hageman factor. Your plasma contains about 7 per cent proteins, or 175,000 mg. All of your Hageman factor is then only one seven-thousandth of the total amount of proteins in your plasma. There is no reason to presume that the Hageman factor is the most rare protein species there is, even though you also contain such bulk as 7000 mg fibrinogen; there may be thousands of proteins like the Hageman factor each in about 25 mg amounts, in each of us, and rarely all the same, from person to person. A dense jungle, and we the blind hunters in it cannot hope to catch any rare and rarely singing bird alive. We can shoot at its voice and hear it stop or change into shrieks of fright. Many a protein changes its song after it has been caught, and turns out to be a mockingbird.

The Prothrombin Complex

Several people believe that prothrombin mocks us, masquerading under disguises that other people call "factors." These other people believe that a definite sequence is needed in clotting, a first factor acting as a potent enzyme that changes its dormant substrate into a second enzyme; this second enzyme in turn would activate its own substrate and change it into the third enzyme, and so on in a seven-step cascade of activations. The order, using the crazy numbers for factors (see Chapter I), is supposed to be: XII, XI, IX, VIII, X, V, prothrombin (Figure 24). On the

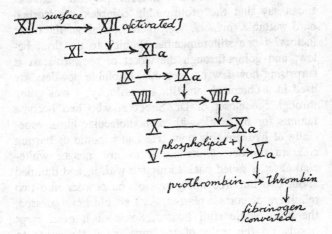

FIGURE 24

other hand, the factors suspected to be part of pro-thrombin by the masquerade group (with Dr. Walter H. Seegers as its leader) are: IX, X, and prothrombin itself if you want to express it that way. All three (as well as a fourth one: Factor VII, that needs some-thing outside your blood to work with, and that I want you to forget immediately) seem to be formed in the liver. If you take tablets to prevent thrombosis, and need weekly checkups with it, you are probably taking a drug that slows down the formation of these four factors. The others will remain undisturbed. Also, the four factors (let us call them the prothrombin complex) can be adsorbed onto all kinds of inorganic powders: aluminum hydroxide, calcium phosphate, barium sulfate. What do these powders have in com-mon?

One late afternoon, sitting in the Mount Sinai lab and in a stupid mood at the same time, I thought of a stupid thing: throw any of these powders in water, and they get wet. Wet, I wondered. They are wettable. I can say that the prothrombin complex is adsorbed onto wettable surfaces. Well then, how about the other factors? I can still remember running to the floor be-low, and going through the closet of chemicals. It is surprising how few nonwettable, insoluble powders are used in a chemical lab. But I was lucky: I was going through the closet of Dr. Sobotka, who had become famous for his work with monomolecular films, espe-cially of hydrophobic ones. He had a bottle of barium stearate powder. Clutching it to my meager white-clad chest, I sailed back to my lab with it, and dumped about two hundred milligrams of the powder into two milliliters of normal plasma. As I should have guessed, the fluffy white stuff floated. Some of it even crept hastily up the walls of the tube, as if desperate to escape. But when I was young, on page 20, I had noticed that the protein (or at least something in the plasma) can make hydrophobic surfaces hydrophilic. So I took a thick glass rod and poked and packed the powder down; first it clumped angrily, but when I rubbed the clumps gently under the surface of the plasma against the test tube wall, the powder seemed suddenly to relax and go sweetly into suspension. I let it stand for about twenty minutes. The technicians left, it was getting dark outside. I centrifuged the tube-ful of milky mixture, collected the cleared plasma, and began testing it. First for prothrombin: it was still normal. Factors VII and X: normal. I took a sample of aged plasma from the freezer. It had been prepared by letting normal plasma sit—and almost literally rot —in a refrigerator for a few weeks. That way, Factor V dies most of all; as a matter of fact, it was discovered that way, and called Labile Factor originally for that reason. It takes abnormally long to clot with thromboplastin. So did my "stearate-treated plasma"; and a mixture of the two was just as abnormal. I had, in other words, removed Factor V with a hydrophobic powder. Much later, I found my sample had also lost its Factor XI and quite a bit of Factor VIII and fibrin-ogen; and later still, that other hydrophobic powders could do the same, and all preferred to adsorb throm-bin rather than prothrombin. I—and you—learned meanwhile that globular protein molecules have their hydrophobic amino acids hidden inside them to keep them dry. I now believe that those which can open easily will do so when they see a hydrophobic surface, and will turn themselves inside out to paste themselves with their fatty hearts onto that surface. Let us call such proteins "apolar" for short, and write the cascade as a zigzag:

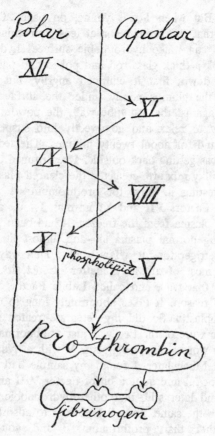

FIGURE 25

Now you can see how all members of the prothrombin complex can hang together. Still, don't think this proves anything. I just hope it may unite the friends that I have in both the Cascade and the Masquerade Party. For they still argue at all coagulation meetings, and always like this:

C(ascade): For each factor, VII, IX, X, prothrombin, we can show you patients specifically missing that one factor and no other.

M(asquerade): These are patients with an abnormal form of prothrombin, which is unable to form your so-called factor or unable to split it off in an active form.

C: We can correct each of the abnormalities of these patients with a different, purified plasma protein.

M: All your purified plasma proteins are derived from a fraction that contained prothrombin and no other activity; this purified prothrombin and its plasma and serum derivatives provide all needs of your patients with abnormal prothrombin.

C: But we have patients that have no prothrombin at all, and who still have normal factors IX, VII, and X and follow the cascade down to the absent prothrombin, where they stop.

M: Those patients have a form of prothrombin that is normal except for the part that has to become thrombin; since you can only measure prothrombin by the thrombin it forms, you think your patients have no prothrombin.

C: When we take your so-called pure prothrombin, we can split off fractions that contain specific VII, IX, and X activity.

M: You are not kidding. You do split them off. You get so rough with my prothrombin that you twist it into pieces, just the way they are normally twisted off during clotting. Where are your Factor IX, your Factor X activity before blood begins to clot? They are just not there, that's all.

C: Just as in your so-called pure prothrombin, they were there in a precursor, an unactivated form.

That's what the whole cascade is about: one factor
activates another.

M: I find that kind of reasoning nonsensical. Just because you cannot find something, you presume it exists
as something else. My so-called pure prothrombin, on
the other hand, has known terminal amino acids, this
one at this end, that one at the other, and I can show
you as I have so often, that after your so-called purification, those terminal amino acids have changed:
you broke something off.

C: Isn't it just as crazy, to say the least, to come up
with four different kinds of abnormal prothrombin
molecule, as it is to assume there are four different
proteins that can be missing?

M: Not at all; look at all the different abnormal hemoglobins, for example. Your cascade is the crazy one.

C: Not at all; look at the cascade of respiration enzymes, passing a hydrogen atom from one to the other.

M: But those are and remain all enzymes; in your
crazy cascade one enzyme attacks one substrate,
makes an enzyme out of that, that one attacks another substrate, makes an enzyme out of that and
so on . . . wouldn't you call that unique, to express
it mildly?

C: Clotting is unique.

Since the greater biochemists must fight like that,
unable to prove just how pure and at the same time
how intact their protein preparations are—what can
we, lesser learned ones, then do but wait? Wait till
someone or something can build the pure molecules
for us and prove they are exactly lifelike? Until then,
the proteins will play with us scientists as much as
we play with them.

Let me give you another example. Many humans,

including me, have tried to study the clotting systems of other animals. How would you do that? If I gave you a lot of citrated, clotted, and any otherwise collected Peking duck blood, and I asked you to see if it contains the Hageman factor, Factors V and VIII? And I also gave you any amount of human plasma, normal or deficient in any known factor you wanted? Here is a line of white space to think in.

I hope you have set up an elegant double series of the human deficient plasmas, added some duck plasma to one series and some plain salt solution to the other series, then calcium chloride to all; and then told yourself that the human samples that got a shorter clotting time by adding the duck plasma, were lacking a factor that was present in the duck plasma. That kind of test has actually been done by many of us. It was first done with Factor XII-deficient plasma; and guess what—adding duck plasma did not just fail to shorten the human clotting time, it prolonged it! And, while it did not affect the clotting of human plasma in a glass test tube, it prolonged also the clotting of intact (unactivated, "glasslessly collected") human plasma in plastic tubes. I read about this at Mount Sinai Hospital, and immediately got permission to order two Peking ducks of my very own.

I did not realize they would be so big, so white, so very serious and sweet. I had heard that a vein in a bird's armpit is a good and painless source. A man helped me to hold the duck on its back, on an operating table. It insisted on bending its neck up and looked me in or between the eyes. I smiled at it. It frowned. I wiped the hot soft inside of its wing with alcohol, rather hastily because the privacy of the downy depths nearly staggered me; but once wet it showed me a good, pink vein, and I obtained a good, clean sample while the duck gently trampled my chest with its size seven yellow slippers. I left my helper feathered and staggering while the two giant wings cast aeronautic shadows.

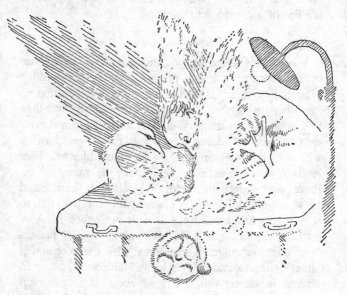

FIGURE 26

The bird's plasma turned out to correct the clotting times of human plasma deficient in Factors V and VIII, and to prolong the clotting times of human plasma deficient in Factors VII, IX, X, XI, or XII. The proper question at this point is: What does this mean? Later, I got two Muscovy ducks, the black and white birds with cauliflower eyes. Where the Peking ducks inhibited, the Muscovies merely failed to correct. Then I took a sample of blood from a wild mallard that someone had found. It in turn differed from the other species. What does any effect of any animal's blood on any other species' blood mean? What does it mean that we cannot easily take a line out of one love poem and put it in another without ruining them both? Big news: we have proved the two poems are different from each other. We have proved that the duck has no Hageman factor; well probably Mr. Hageman has no duck factor either, but both are doing fine.

Mr. Hageman and birds do have one thing in common: their plasma does not clot much faster in glass than in plastic. This alone should not suffice to keep people with Hageman factor deficiency from marrying a Peking duck; we cannot even guess what is compatible with what. All we can say is: Any species that has survived until now is well adapted to last a while. A doctor once asked me, "How is a duck's prothrombin?" I said, "How do you mean, how?" "Well, is it high, or low, or normal?" "I guess it is normal, for ducks. How would you test it?" "Well, I think you could compare it to human blood." But you can't: the human unit of prothrombin is the amount that, converted into thrombin, will make a cubic millimeter of human blood clot in a certain time. And that time is based on the speed that human thrombin has been found to convert a certain amount of human plasma or fibrinogen with. To compare these units with the unknown duck blood is like trying to express your opinion of a book in terms of grams per second. You must first find out if the precursor of thrombin in ducks is something like prothrombin. You must take a few hundred ducks that do not complain of frequent nosebleeding or of blood in their stools, and establish the normal range of whatever it is you think you are measuring. Only then can you begin to look for ducks that are abnormal, try to find out if there is a factor they lack, obtain a family history; in short, you must spend as much time as has been devoted to humans and their various inborn deficiencies before you can start giving names, like Christmas Factor, after a duck by the name of Christmas who lacks it.

The point is that every protein molecule inside a duck—not including the piece of human fingertip it may have in its stomach, of course—is a duck protein, and it is very unlikely to find a successful career in a human system of proteins. All parts of the duck are adapted to all other parts, and always were, no matter how much they all changed every so many millions of years. They changed like the words in a folk-tale do: every change of one word compensated by some other, so that at no time utter nonsense remains, though sometimes a few emptied words are dragged along for a while before they are dropped. Maybe the Hageman factor has become such an empty thing out of the past. Certainly we must not expect any protein to have the same meaning in two species, we must not expect the blood of an animal to correct some hereditary human deficiency exactly, and even if it does appear to correct, we must not be misled into thinking that it corrected with something identical to what was lacking in the human. For example, it was found that (see page 63) our blood contains a labile factor: Factor V. Beef plasma corrects Factor V deficiency very well; even aged beef plasma, and even beef serum does; neither time nor the act of clotting seems to destroy beef Factor V, and it is often used as a nice strong source for it. But human Factor V disappears completely during and after our blood clots, so the two Factors V are completely different. Even the brain

extracts used so often in clotting work seem to remember who they are: they were found to work most
rapidly with plasma from their own species. Still,
many experiments are described in which rabbit brain
powder is mixed with human plasma and beef serum.
Such mixed-up test tube zoos must produce wild grade
C jungle movies for those small enough to see; for us
macroscopic things only some average outcome can
be observed: a clotting time, a number, and always
a misleading one.

Proteins and Heredity

That proteins in test tubes play with us is merely
funny; much more serious are the games they play
within the hereditarily sick. Certain diseases are inherited, just as the color of your hair was. Somewhere
you must contain a memory that works day and night
to keep your cells from making a different color of
hair from time to time. Since you know more than I
do about heredity and genes and all that, and there
are better books about them, here is only a sketch:

When things grow, their cells divide. When a cell
divides, its nucleus divides first and, within the nucleus, each *chromosome* is replicated first. A chromosome is a "string of genes," so for a chromosome to
divide, each of its genes has to divide and the two
halves have to complete themselves somehow, each to
become a copy of the original. A *gene* contains a molecule shaped like a twisted ladder and called *d*eoxyri-
bo*n*ucleic *a*cid, or DNA for short. Each rung of the
ladder is made of one pair of substances held together
by hydrogen bonds, and only two kinds of pairs exist:
adenine paired with thymine, and guanine paired with

cytosine. Call them a, t, g, and c, and you can write
ladders like this:

```
. . . c a t a t t a g c g g g . . .
. . . g t a t a a t c g c c c . . .
```

When the gene's ladder splits along its weakest
bonds (down the middle of all rungs), each half rung
on each half ladder will then pick up a new half rung
from its environment, so that eventually each half
ladder will look like the old whole ladder. The message, locked in the sequence of rungs, is read by a
complicated system of ribonucleic acids (RNA molecules), and will lead to the production of a protein
molecule wherein each one amino acid was dictated
by one sequence of *three* rungs in the original DNA.
Pretending that capital letters represent amino acids,
and that the following codes exist: cat = L, ggg = E,
att = O, and agc = V, then the ladder section written
above would spell . . . LOVE, and the message to
make LOVE is passed by this particular DNA molecule from the nucleus to the body (the cytoplasm) of
the cell. And as long as there are the needed RNA
molecules around, the message will keep flowing out,
and LOVE will be made, copy after copy. But change
one rung—and that can apparently happen by the jump
of only one proton!—so that let us say the fifth digit
on the bottom becomes a g instead of an a, and the
set it belongs in becomes tga, which would mean i
instead of o, and the word will now be live instead
of love; quite a difference, especially when it keeps
being printed wrong in the entire book. A rare long
word in a large text may not suffer too much from
such a mutation—covering can afford to become kover-
ing, or coverink, but it may also become hovering, or
cohering, and so destroy the entire sentence in which

it stands. The more responsibility a word has in a text—or an enzyme in an animal—and the more vital the spot where it is hit, the less chance such a text has to express its intended meaning.

It is not necessarily the quantity of wrong or absent protein that does the damage. You can print a whole book with one of its most frequently used words spelled wrong, such as "t" instead of "it," and still not warp its story. There are people who have no albumins in their blood; that means the major part of all their blood proteins is absent. If you consider that albumin is a small protein, responsible for a good amount of osmotic pressure in your blood, and for the binding of specific molecules such as fatty acids, you may be surprised to know that people with this enormous misprint suffer very little from it.

On the other hand, a most tragic error can occur, for example, in a DNA molecule of one chromosome going by the name of X. You may know that a sperm and an egg each have a set of chromosomes, and when they embrace and fuse create what you could call the first cell of the child; but that the sperm, instead of two X chromosomes, has an X and a Y (as it is called). Let us write the X chromosome with the error as X′, the prime mark after the X meaning the sick gene or DNA molecule; the mother has then XX′, and the father has XY if he is normal. The DNA molecule that I mean is the one that passes the message to make antihemophilic globulin, or Factor VIII as we now call it. In the mother of our story, one X chromosome does pass that message all through her body, and she makes enough Factor VIII to appear normal, even though the X′ chromosome is idle or passes the message to make some distorted thing that does not function as Factor VIII should at all. If she and her normal husband have a son, that must mean he got a Y chromosome and he can only get that one from his father. The one that goes with it must come from his mother and must therefore be either the normal X chromosome, or the X′ one. This boy will then have no DNA molecules that can pass the message to make any normal Factor VIII: he is a hemophiliac—or he will be lucky and get the healthy one of the two X-chromosomes his mother had, and he will be as normal and healthy as his father. His sisters will all seem healthy, but they may be XX, or XX′. The XX′ girls are called carriers: they carry the disease but do not show it.

Figure 27 is a little diagram of this disaster, and you surely can continue the picture on your own. It may be fun, unless you contain X′ chromosomes yourself, because then, not only is the certainty bad, the uncertainty around it is. It is easy to tell a YX from a YX′: YX does not bleed into his joints, does not need transfusions with his tooth extractions, does not have to play with soft toys only, can marry any girl who loves him. But how can you tell XX′ from XX before it is too late? Very many tests have been developed to refine measurement of Factor VIII, hoping to tell normal from just-below-normal levels. So far, the best we can say is that, on the average, carrier girls have less than the full 100 per cent of normal Factor VIII. That is of no help to any one, real live young sister of a hemophiliac, or the daughter of a possible carrier.

Frankly, we don't even know for sure that any hemophiliac really lacks Factor VIII, or maybe has an abnormally shaped Factor VIII; he may very well not lack anything, but have an extra protein that acts as an inhibitor to his normal Factor VIII. In that case, he has an error not in the DNA that orders Factor

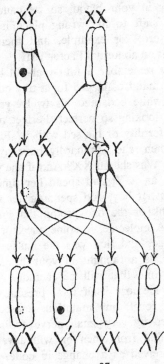

FIGURE 27

VIII to be printed, but in quite another DNA molecule. Why can't we tell a difference between those two
so very different abnormalities? Because there is no
visible gap in the blood where Factor VIII should be,
in any of these patients; we just can't split the plasma
proteins up fine enough, with any electrophoresis, any
chromatography, to show that here is a line or fraction
of protein in all normal plasma samples, and here it is
empty in this boy's plasma, here it is only half-filled
in this carrier. We just don't have a "Factor VIII
place," or any other place corresponding with one en-

zyme activity in your blood, so we cannot see your Factor VIII shift to the wrong place in an electrophoresis pattern, for example, and then say: look, this fellow has an abnormal Factor VIII.

I suddenly remember a four-year-old boy, his legs in braces, his hand bandaged for a tiny cut, as he was sitting on a white bed, and his twelve-year-old sister standing and looking so perfect. Perfect or imperfect? Cursed with fertility or blessed with it? From the way she looked then, she can hardly have avoided being married now. Was she an XX? And if she was an XX', did she have an X'Y, and spend her time rushing to hospitals with her boy, and spending her money there as well? Think of the one proton that may have hit that one DNA molecule, in some ancestor a few hundred years ago, and that was the cause of it all. It was as small as a thought in your brain that fades unspoken—or one that will never fade. As a matter of fact, your memory itself is at present regarded as a complex of local, tiny mutations caused maybe by protons carried by very small nerve endings to some nucleic acid that from then on will always pass the message it received as a change in code, a new protein, printed and reprinted to remind you of that one time when that one proton hit you right there. But doesn't this make you feel like one giant amplifier? And an amplifier of what? Mostly of randomness: One cosmic ray from outer space may hit you, depending where you are sitting right now, hit you in one proton that will heat up a few of your water molecules less than one-thousandth of a degree maybe, or hit you in one proton that will raise a thought appearing to come from nowhere and that will die unused, or that will start a dream never to be forgotten, or a disease in your yet unborn child, a disease never seen before that will spread from you through mankind. That is

what I call amplification, and frankly, meeting it in
a patient has become too big an event for me, too big
and irreversible an injustice to face helplessly every
day. I am not a doctor, I am a Ph.D., and all I want to
concentrate on is facts, not reality. And indirectly, I
may help a bit; certainly more than I ever did directly.

You may wonder what exactly I am doing now that
can be of any use. I did promise at the end of Chapter
I that I would tell you, and I shall be relieved to do
so now.

Monomolecular Films

It started in 1947, when I bought a very fat book,
because I felt lonely. It was late in spring, in New
Brunswick, a strange little town in a strange land. Ab-
solutely foreign birds were arriving from somewhere,
to descend upon nameless plants and whistle anony-
mous phrases. I had not seen my fiancée since I had
escaped from Holland, seven years that spring, and
there was nothing around me but spring itself to remember her with. The robins sang like false Dutch
merels, and the blue jays shrieked almost like *vlaamse
gaaien;* even some people were sometimes like someone. I had rented a small American room. Its American things did not speak in my presence. Whatever I
arranged before leaving it in the morning—a notebook
opened, an old letter propped up again, an army knife
on top of a jar of marmalade instead of beside it—
when I returned at night prepared to be surprised all
failed as soon as I opened the door. So I bought this
book. It weighed seven pounds, and for a while I
could come home to take this rather heavy source of
astonishment onto my lap.

Its name was *Medical Physics* (Vol. 1, ed. Otto

Glasser, et al.; Year Book Publications, Chicago, Illinois, 1944). There was a chapter in it by Dr. H. Sobotka about the study of films one molecule thick. It changed my life enough to tell you about it; don't worry, it will all come back to blood. One way to study such films is by creating them on top of water, like this. You make a trough and make all its insides water-repellent. You fill it almost to overflowing with a barium salt solution in water. You also have a solution of stearic acid in benzene. You place a drop of that on top of the barium solution. The drop does not mix, but floats and spreads immediately over the whole surface, where the benzene evaporates; the stearic acid molecules, which have wettable acid heads, will stick them into the water and make a barium salt with the barium ions they find around them. The stearic acid tails, however, are hydrophobic, so they will insist on sticking out of the water. Now you can round up these forlornly floating sailboats in several ways, for example by dragging a floating thread across, or pushing a bar, or by allowing a wax paper or thin plastic float that spans the entire width of the trough to be pulled by a thread and a tiny weight over a pulley, as in this sketch:

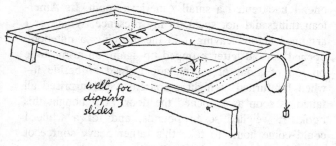

FIGURE 28

If you do it this way, you will see the float move and then be stopped as if by an invisible elastic force: you have compressed the film of barium stearate until all molecules are packed and upright, side by side. Now you dip a hydrophobic metal piece of mirror very slowly into the stearate film; it is like dipping a finger into a soft balloon. Where you poke it, it gives and it coats your finger like a glove. But the mirror is hydrophobic, and the hydrophobic surface of the stearate will stick to the mirror when you pull it up and drag more film along to fold over the first, as in this sketch:

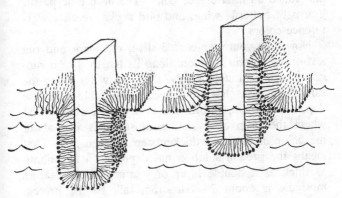

FIGURE 29

As you can see, each dip gives you a double layer of molecules. If you collect ten, your mirror will begin to look pale yellow, and with more it will become tawny, then deep wine red, then purple, violet, and then blue. If you do those last dips less and less deep, you will get colored steps, each change standing for one more double layer or twice the length of a stearate molecule. The colors, like those of spilled oil drops spreading on water and fleetingly decorating gutters and ocean waves, are caused by the white sunlight being reflected at the top and bottom of the oil film at the same time. The waves of light traveling the long way through to the bottom of the film and out again will have fallen behind those reflected directly at the surface of the film, and if their wavelengths happen to be equal but with the one delayed exactly enough to oscillate in opposite direction from the other, the pair will kill each other. You can see then that the white light has lost a color; the mixture that remains is caused by this interference of light waves, and called an interference color. The deep blue purple greens of butterfly wings and bird necks are also interference colors.

Now take your step-coated sliver of mirror and run a drop of protein solution along its length, like a runner covering all steps partly, then run water along the same path that has now become wettable with the deposited protein, and then let it dry. You will see that where the drop once ran, each step has just about the color of the next thicker step (Figure 30). That means the protein solution has deposited a film about as thick as a double layer of stearate. Each stearate molecule is about 24 Ångström tall, so the protein molecule must have been about 48 Ångström tall or fat. Also, you have now measured something that is too small to be seen through a microscope, and you did it without any real instruments. Langmuir, who invented this trick and many others, often worked with strings, wax, crank case oil properly aged, and a window with northern exposure. I found the name of this very great man too late, when he had turned away from all this, to ways of making rain, and then to the greatest and simplest experiment of all: he died.

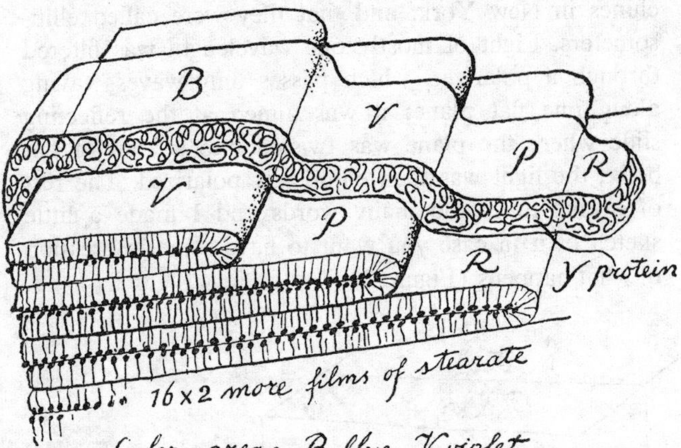
B
V
V
P
P
R
R
Y protein
16 x 2 more films of stearate
Color areas B blue, V violet,
P purple, R red and Y yellow.

FIGURE 30

Maybe the time of doing great things with little means died with him. One day I myself discovered something simple: I let water condense on plates and it revealed what? in the whiteness of the misted surface where protein films were adsorbed. Then I found this had been done before, long, long ago. By Langmuir, of course. Anyway, when I read of his work in the fat book in the small room, with many too recent war years of pieces of string and slivers of mirror behind me, I preferred to believe that any effort to surpass his conclusions without surpassing his intelligence would be quite expensive: I wanted a machine. I wanted it to show me a lot more accurately what surfaces would do to blood proteins; a machine that would take a barium stearate stepcoated slide and record its change in thickness as it adsorbed proteins out of plasma. I discovered there were two such machines in New York, and that they were called ellipsometers. Light of mostly one wavelength was filtered through a polarizer, which passes only waves waving along one flat plane; it was aimed at the reflecting slide where the plane was twisted into a kind of flat helix; the light was then elliptically polarized. The rest of events takes too many words and I made a little sketch of it in case you want to have some impression of what happens (Figure 31).

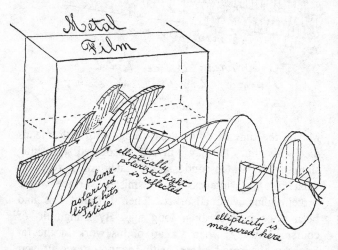

FIGURE 31

Meanwhile, summer passed. I saw it pass on Sundays, and on weekdays after work, when I would lie on a small wild piece of grounds behind the hospital, among suddenly tall and blooming weeds. And then my fiancée arrived. We were married the next day with a friend and two internes in white as witnesses and audience; the maples turned red; goldfinches went south; and an ellipsometer manufacturer came to see us. Our laboratory in the hospital at that time was a part-time room. Half of it was a bed for basal metabolism tests. When the bed contained no patient, we had a board on it for a table. The visiting manufacturer, for whom the board was removed so that he

FIGURE 32

could sit on the bed, must have realized that our interest in his eleven-thousand-dollar machine was still academic. Ten years later, however, I happened to be working in the Mount Sinai Hospital coagulation lab, with the office of Dr. Sobotka and his ellipsometer only a few steps away. Both, and others, were very helpful. I did only a few, very clumsy measurements, and the results were so confusing that I wanted more. So finally, after another five years went by and I came to work at the Veterans Administration Hospital in Brooklyn, I asked for an ellipsometer all my own, and

I got it, about a year later. Meanwhile, I had visited a cousin of mine who worked at the Bell Telephone research laboratories. He happened to show me some glass slides that he had coated with tantalum and then anodized. This electric oxydation process forms a coating of tantalum oxide on the reflecting surface that is so thin it shows beautiful interference colors, the color depending on the voltage that he anodized the slides with. Just what I needed: a lasting surface with exactly the kind of optical properties I needed, and no need for dipping slides fifteen times in a trough to make a surface that could only be used once.

The machine was beautiful, too. When it had been rolled in, unpacked, installed, and plugged in, the mercury lamp burning, small lights reflecting in satin finish metal and gray hammered enamel, and the violet slide sitting in the middle of it all, where the cuvette full of solution stirred gently by a helical glass rod slowly began to ooze and spill its contents over the instrument—well, the leaky cuvette was only one of very few problems. The main trouble was that the meter, from which we had to read numbers at rapid intervals, oscillated each time a particle of dust would hinder the light reflected by the slide. We needed a recording system to get good curves, and in another year we got it.

In all this time, the world of clotting had not stood still. When I first heard of the ellipsometer, Factor IX was the latest discovery. When I came to Mount Sinai, Factors X and XI were a few years old and XII had just appeared in print. So, obviously, all my efforts to discover how surface acted on blood before Mr. Hageman became known, were as good as looking for a horse in a hoofprint. By the time my machine began to record, Factor XII was already generally believed to go onto glass first; Factor XI was then supposed to go onto this activated XII and take it off.

The first curve we made with it—the very first, with the gentleman who attached the recorder still attached to it—was going to be one of plasma. We turned on the lamp, placed a good cuvette of buffer solution in the light path, clamped one of our violet slides in it, turned on the stirrer, peeked through a telescope, adjusted seven knobs, two dials, and a lever, switched the final knob to "recorder," watched the pen write a rather mossy but flattish lawn, added a few drops of intact plasma to the solution, and watched the pen first sketch a bunch of sticks, and then, quickly, a steep mountain that kept going up fast and then more and more slowly—Factor XII being adsorbed? And then, believe it or not, very gently the mountain began to slope down, until after half an hour about a quarter of it was gone (Figure 33). Removal of Factor XII by Factor XI?

Of course this seemed too good to be true. But within two weeks we showed that intact plasma always gave curves like that, and plasma that was first shaken with glass and then centrifuged, so that it had already gone through all the adventures of going on a surface and coming off again—plasma like that would also show a mountain of adsorption on our slide, but nothing would come off after that, even if we added intact plasma next. Probably, other proteins were glad to be adsorbed if no intact Factor XII claimed the surface first. Later, a kind doctor sent us a Factor XII-deficient patient from North Carolina. With his plasma, again the machine drew a mountain, and the top stayed flat: adsorption, not followed by removal. Removal only followed when we added purified Factor XII, obtained from another kind doctor.

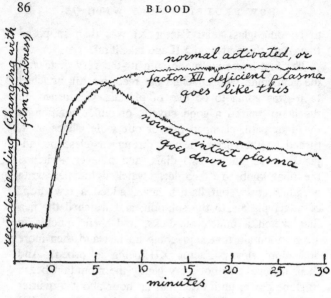

FIGURE 33

And only when we premixed the Factor XII-deficient plasma with Factor XII and then stuck it in our machine, did we get a normal curve: mountain, then gentle downslope. Good. But did our experiments fit the theory well? Think!

If you do have it all figured out I have bad news for you: just this week we did some more experiments, and I now *think* the following happens. It is known that activated Factor XII goes to work not only on Factor XI, but also on a protein called plasminogen, making a protein-digesting enzyme out of it that is called plasmin. Plasmin has a special appetite for fibrinogen and fibrin. In our machine, and probably in ordinary test tubes too, first fibrinogen is adsorbed onto the surface, Factor XII becomes activated (maybe on top of it, or somewhere else) and in turn activates the plasminogen molecules in solution as they pass by, converting them to plasmin. The plasmin then bites the heads off the fibrinogen at the surface. So perhaps, after all, adsorbed fibrinogen or its remaining stubblefield does act as a platelet glue: what else will the platelets find to stick to?

Hemoglobin

I may have given you the feeling that hereditary protein abnormalities—those mutations that are often called "molecular diseases"—either fail to tell us definitely if there is really a protein malformed or absent (the problem in hemophilia), or else fail to tell us if the lack or abnormality has any significance to the body walking around with it (the problem in absence of albumin or of Factor XII). In the misty field of blood clotting, our excuse is that all proteins but fibrin are invisible no matter how purely absent they are, and we can only find something by stepping in it and slipping. People who work with hemoglobins are luckier: here is a protein, deeply painted, locked up neatly in red blood cells that can be centrifuged, collected, washed, and then broken to release a 30 per cent solution of the red stuff; only a little bit of the cells can be called contamination and it is not red. No wonder hemoglobin could be crystallized and its shape determined by complex but elegant means.

Normal hemoglobin, called hemoglobin A (or Hb A for short) looks like the next sketch.

It is built like Siamese twins, each twin with a molecular weight of 33,000 (times the weight of one hydrogen atom) and containing about three hundred amino acids. These three hundred form two chains,

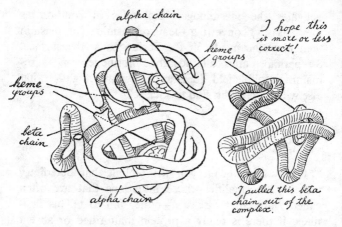

FIGURE 34

called alpha and beta, so that the whole molecule has
two alpha and two beta chains. Fingerprints of the
best-known abnormal hemoglobins, Hb S and Hb C,
show that they each differ from A in only one amino
acid of each beta chain. In a spot where A has a
hydrophilic one called glutamic acid, S has a hydrophobic one called valine. You can break Hb into its
four chains, and then, for example, put a radioactive
atom on each chain. Pretend you do this with Hb A,
and then mix all pieces with loose chains of Hb S.
You can then allow new combinations to form. One
product you will get is typical Hb S but with radioactivity on its alpha chains. What does that prove?

It proves that the alpha chains of Hb S are normal.
It is the hydrophobic amino acid in the beta chains
that causes disaster. At body temperature, when hydrophobic bonds are strongest, that abnormal valine
probably is forced by the water around it to form a
sick hydrophobic bond with another, normal, valine

in the same molecule, and the sick bond distorts the entire molecule into such a shape that it can pack tight with other Hb S molecules, especially when they have given up their oxygen, as they must when passing slowly through oxygen-hungry tissues. There the Hb S molecules inside the red cells stack and stack to form giant complexes, actually long red crystals, that distort the entire red cell bodies so that they become sickle-shaped (Figure 35). And the sickle-

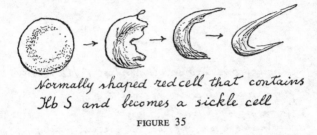

Normally shaped red cell that contains Hb S and becomes a sickle cell

FIGURE 35

shaped cells tangle up into clumps that clog circulation and can cause death. Sickle cell disease is a terrible thing to inherit, especially when you are aware of the infuriatingly small mutation that causes it.

But it may not be all bad, if you inherit it only from one parent. You may remember that, in general, for each of your "properties" you probably get two genes: one from your father, one from your mother. And that, if both genes are the same, you can call yourself homozygous for that property. Otherwise you are heterozygous. Well, patients with sickle cell disease are homozygous; you can say they are SS. But those with sickle cell trait are heterozygous, because one gene is normal; they are SA. Electrophoresis of hemoglobin from AA people will give you just one band; electrophoresis of hemoglobin from SS people will also give you one band but in a different spot; AS people, however, will give you two spots, one where A belongs and one for S (Figure 36). That one ab-

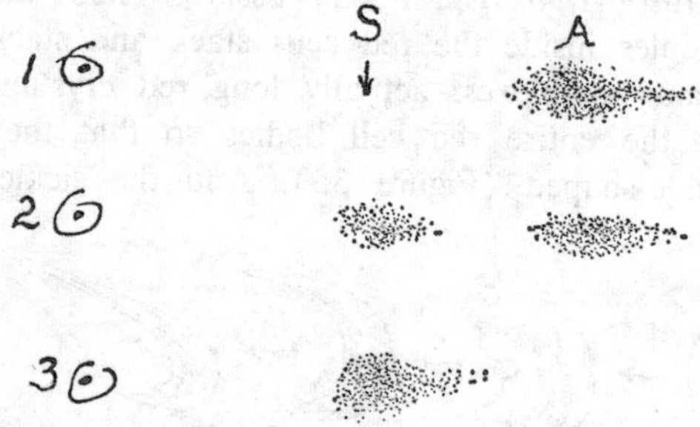

1: blood from normal control (Hb A only);
2: from patient with A and S;
3: from patient with S only.
  Samples were applied at circled dots;
  then current turned on.

FIGURE 36

normal amino acid in S distorts the molecule apparently enough to give it a different speed in an electric field.

It is the SA people who can be lucky under certain conditions. In certain regions of Africa, there are more SA patients than has been thought reasonable, until it was shown that fewer SA than AA children died of a severe form of malaria. Their sickle cell trait apparently protects them. Of course the luck of being an AS only stands out against the bad luck of being anything else. When an AS boy marries an AS girl, they can have normal AA babies that run a high chance of being killed by the lethal malaria, or SS

babies that will die of sickle cell disease; or AS babies
that are again the lucky ones, as long as malaria lasts.

Thrombosis and the Hageman Factor

Many more people than we think may be walking
among us with a much more positive mutation: those
with Hageman factor deficiency, already discussed in
Chapter I. This "disease" causes no bleeding and is
so harmless that "sufferers" are rarely discovered, so
we probably do not have a chance yet to collect enough
biographic material on them to make sure that they
are surviving better than others would under exactly
the same conditions. But so far it looks as if there
just may be less heart disease among them. A main
cause of heart disease is thrombosis of coronary vessels—the vessels that must carry oxygen-rich blood
into the heart muscles. Thrombosis—the growth of a
thrombus—is the formation of an awfully real thing,
the kind a pathologist searches a corpse's blood vessels for, and presto! there it is, looking like a live slug,
a slick parasite with a tough gray head of fused platelets and a deep red tail of red blood cells trapped in
a cast of fibrin. Such an obvious thing leads even scientists to think it must have an obvious cause. A
thrombus looks like a clot, so it is obviously caused
by the clotting mechanism. It is attached at a spot on
the blood vessel wall with its head, from where it
grows. It is obviously caused by a change in the blood
vessel wall. It starts with platelets sticking to that
spot, so it is caused by having too many sticky platelets. Most people who believed passionately enough
in any one cause the most were able to prove to themselves that they were right. I, for example, want to

stress right now that the following has been found:
a) activated Hageman factor makes platelets more
sticky; and b) people who suffer from thrombosis
probably have activated Hageman factor circulating in
their blood. How it became activated is another question; certainly not by contact with glass, but maybe
by fatty acids that entered the blood and could for
some reason not be bound by albumin and made harmless. Anyway, if this is all true, then the "patients"
with Hageman factor deficiency may rarely get heart
disease (coronary thrombosis at least) because they
contain nothing that can be activated and make
platelets sticky. Next, you can imagine how the Hageman deficients of this world, popping up as isolated
mutations here and there, will fail to drop dead at a
rather early age.* Just the fact that most American
males still manage to have some children before dying
of heart failure, prevents Normalman from dying out
and Hageman from taking over entirely. The idle question then becomes: how did Normalman ever come
to be burdened by such a useless protein?

The answer must be far behind us, when we drifted
away from the spineless animals and fled onto the
dry and frightful land. In those days, or in those ani-

---

* A patient was brought to a hospital recently because he
had just suffered a heart attack. Before starting the usual treatment with clot-preventing drugs, his doctors had a clotting time
done. It was quite long, so they invited me to join. The clotting
time was corrected by all abnormal plasmas we had around,
except by Factor XII-deficient samples, and later Dr. Ratnoff
confirmed that our patient almost totally lacked Factor XII. If
the heart attack was really caused by a thrombus (and this
cannot be demonstrated, since both our patient and another similar case recently reported are still alive and well!), maybe the
inability to activate plasminogen in the bloodstream when it
is needed balanced the low ability to form fibrin; little fibrin
was formed, but none was digested. Meanwhile, the theory may
survive only as long as the patients do.

mals, contact of a foreign surface with blood still affected whole blood cells and not a dissolved molecule in the plasma. Such cells, which practically explode on contact, are called thrombocytes. Like human platelets, they plug up wounds, but they have nuclei and look more like amoebae. Is there any mechanism in those cells that we can recognize as a forerunner of our own dissolved contact-sensitive system? Or, to go all the way, is there anything like clotting that protects an amoeba?

Yes. There is a lot. Some amoebae, when hurt, were found to bleed away if placed in heparin, a powerful anticoagulant to all bloods. An amoeba from the ocean will bleed to death if calcium is taken away from its natural world; as you know, our blood needs calcium to clot also. As the amoeba "clots," an enzyme appears to be formed that can make others clot; it is in some ways like our thrombin. But there is a more delicate family likeness that I think I have found myself, so I must show it to you in more detail.

If we go back to my favorite zigzag system of clotting, and what I said on page 63, I can expand a bit. I said there that the "apolar" proteins are "those which can open easily" at a hydrophobic surface and "will turn themselves inside out to paste themselves with their fatty hearts onto that surface." In the zigzag, it looks as if there is no hydrophobic surface to start it all with. But how would this be: Factor XII is adsorbed onto a polar (wettable) surface. There it changes shape, because, after all, that must happen when some protein is "activated": it changes shape. As it changes, Factor XII exposes its more hydrophobic amino acids; and this is what Factor XI, an apolar molecule, has been waiting for: it turns itself inside out and pastes itself onto the fat belly of XII, if you don't mind. Possibly, the pattern of electric charges that the now distorted Factor XI exposes on its wettable back attracts Factor IX, and when that one fits itself onto XI, hydrophobic amino acids of IX will be exposed that will make VIII come over and turn inside out. And so on; or if IX, X, and pro-thrombin are part of one molecule, you can see the whole business as a series of attacks by apolar proteins until they reach and expose the apolar heart of prothrombin, called thrombin.

I published this idea about a year ago, and I wrote the draft for the pages you just read much later, of course. But last week—that is a week before the moment I am typing this text as you see it now—I had a telephone conversation with Dr. Ratnoff in Cleveland, the discoverer of Mr. Hageman, and guess what he told me . . . that he found his purified Hageman factor became less soluble in water, and more hydrophobic, when it was activated! You are kidding, I exclaimed; I am never kidding, he answered. Coming all the way from Cleveland to me in New York made the news even more dramatic, sufficiently so to believe in it for as long as the next few paragraphs.

Now, leave clotting and go back inside the cell. There, an important set of experiments was done about fifty years ago and improved about thirty years later. It goes like this:

1. Looking through a microscope, you stick a very fine glass needle into a cell, and inject a drop of oil. Leave the drop attached to the tip of the needle and after a little while, very slowly suck some of the drop back in. You will first see the drop get somewhat smaller, then instead of continuing, it will start to wrinkle.

2. Do the same with another cell, right after you hurt

it a bit somewhere away from where the needle will be. This time, the oil drop will hardly need to get any smaller at all before it starts wrinkling.

3. Do the same as in 2., but wait a while after hurting the cell and only then start injecting the oil drop. This time you have to suck the drop back until it is quite a bit smaller again before it wrinkles; 3. is very much like 1.

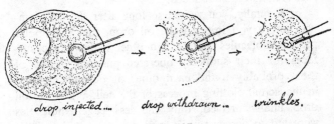

drop injected...   drop withdrawn..   wrinkles.

FIGURE 37

What is the explanation of all this? In 1., all kinds of more or less apolar proteins were adsorbed onto the hydrophobic surface of the oil drop. When the drop was sucked back and its surface thus made smaller, the less apolar, or more springy protein molecules could let go, rewind themselves back into their old shapes with their wettable amino acids covering their hearts again, and they could return to their wettable surroundings in the cytoplasm. Only when the drop had become so small that the most apolar protein molecules, those which always have to turn themselves hopelessly inside-out at a nonwettable surface, had become packed tight, and when their bodies, stretched out and clamped tightly onto the shrinking surface, began to buckle, did the drop begin to wrinkle.

In 2., the bit of damage you did to the cell caused a

rapid change in its body. You disrupted some delicate web of proteins, lipids, and nucleic acids, and set free an internal shower of the fragile, "apolar" type of proteins. These were attracted by the surface of the oil drop that you injected so soon afterward, and they all turned inside out and stretched out rigidly over the drop's surface, crowding each other so much that they had to buckle: the drop wrinkled before its surface area had to be reduced.

In 3. finally, you waited so long after the cell damage before you injected the oil drop, that the apolar protein molecules had to find other hydrophobic surfaces for their suddenly liberated passions. Many of them probably found each other or became engaged in the actual clotting process of the cell. When the oil drop finally arrived, only the less eager molecules were left to descend on it, and when you reduced the size of the drop they let go with ease and floated away into the altered cytoplasm, meanwhile coiling back into their old wettable shell-shaped selves. And the drop did not wrinkle.

What made the torn web cry such fatty tears—if it did? Perhaps the rip you made in the outer cell membrane helped. Membranes, as you will see in the next chapter, contain much phospholipid, and a phospholipid molecule has a polar head, like a fatty acid but containing phosphorus, with a couple of long fatty apolar tails. Throw a bunch of phospholipid molecules in water, and they will immediately bunch all their tails together with hydrophobic bonds, meanwhile facing the water with their charged heads. In a cell membrane, these molecules are probably neatly arranged in double layers, like the barium stearate double films on the dipped slides of page 78. Two such double layers probably form the two slices of bread between

which the proteins of the membrane are sandwiched.
One cut across, and not only the spread of proteins
will ooze out, but also the double layers of phospholipid, breaking up into tiny double-walled hollow
balls, and into single-walled ones described on the
previous page; they are all called micelles. Then, the
apolar proteins close to the soft small micelles which
they resemble in a way—each protein molecule being
a kind of micelle in itself—may turn inside out and
break into the heart of the micelle, liberating more
phospholipid molecules to react with more apolar
protein molecules, and so on, until no more hydrophobic bonding sites are available.

It just so happens that my zigzag of plasma clotting
can be defined in almost the same way. It so happens
that wherever the arrows in it go to the right, the reaction is helped by fatty acids at first and by phospholipid micelles later; and it so happens that, after Factors V and VIII—the especially apolar ones—have reacted, they die, just the way the apolar proteins of the
cell body are briefly active upon damage to the cell
and then die. As a matter of fact, the stuff we so
clumsily extract from all kinds of tissue, and that
contains a rather dead mixture of phospholipids and
protein, labeled together as "thromboplastin" and
able to convert prothrombin rapidly to thrombin under the right conditions—this messy stuff I now believe
is not normally present in the cells. The cells make it
in a few seconds while we destroy them to prepare
our extract. Why do they make their thromboplastin
so rapidly? Because most cells are not just covered
with a membrane, but laminated and larded with
them. One pinprick will go through stacks of sand-
wiches at the same time. From a prick in your skin,
millions of such tiny disasters will liberate enough

thromboplastin to form enough thrombin right there in your plasma, to make enough platelets passing by sticky enough to plug up the prick. Then, the damaged platelets will remember their heritage, and liberate their own powerful phospholipid, pearling as micelles out of their membranes, and cause more clotting. But they are late, and of the apolar clotting factors—which they do adsorb preferentially!—that come off them, probably only a little Factor V, VIII, and fibrinogen participate. In the olden days that was different. In the horseshoe crab, for example, the exploding thrombocytes probably contain all factors needed for clotting. And then more and more factors began to be formed outside the thrombocytes and to be poured into the plasma directly. Mutation after mutation, the plasma factors changed. So did the old factors in our tissues; the tissue cells went more or less their own way, and their thromboplastin, as a result, works differently on our prothrombin than our own plasma does. Maybe only those animals have survived whose two systems, cell and plasma, could still work together while being jostled by mutations. Even fibrinogen keeps mutating. The small peptides that are snapped off it by thrombin have been analyzed for different species of vertebrates. The percentage of amino acids in their peptides, differing from those in our own peptides, can be plotted against how long ago the species is thought to have appeared on earth. You get a very nice curve that way, and if you pull it down to the point where all amino acids in the peptides differ from ours, you happen to land in a time when the very first vertebrates are supposed to have appeared. The biological conclusion that this mathematical game led to then is that the formation of any peptides from fibrinogen as it clotted started with the vertebrates; but whether or not that is a logical conclusion, you will be able to tell me as well as I can tell you.

Another curve, just as theoretical, has been made for a respiration enzyme, cytochrome C. It is a little like hemoglobin, but it is so widely distributed over living things that you can go back to yeast and calculate its percentage of difference from our cytochrome C. Then, of course, your line goes much farther back in years to when yeast was created. And the same can be done for the short time that hemoglobin has existed. For example, man and gorilla hemoglobin differ only in three or four amino acids—so little that there may be perfectly healthy gorillas and people walking around right now with each other's mutations. Such a change in the hemoglobin only will not make a gorilla human enough to think twice about it, though. And at the extreme end again, man and fish hemoglobin have only about one amino acid left in common. That must have taken a very long time to happen, because the chance keeps increasing that a mutation will hit an amino acid that it had hit before, so that the percentage of deviation will not have changed this time. Hundreds of millions of years will have to pass until just that last rung of the responsible DNA molecule will be hit that has not yet been touched. And very rough calculations tell that about fifteen million years, give or take four million, must pass between mutations.

It may have struck you that, in a way, all mutations I talked about caused a loss: a loss of the ability to make a protein that functions fittingly within the system it belongs with. Billions of years ago, when we were young and green, but suddenly lost the ability to form the chlorophyll that was supposed to make sugar for us out of the air, we learned to eat the creatures that still had that ability. Thus, pale but active, we learned to live with our new sickness.

The ability to adjust to each new hereditary disease must have been there when we were still single, reproducing protein and nucleic acid molecules. You remember what happened to Hb A when it became Hb S: its molecules started packing together in long crystal-like structures, just because their new shape demanded it. We may have grown like that, onto specific spots of rock with electric charges on their surface just right to form patterns from the molecules of protein they adsorbed, forming lacy films tied together with hydrogen and hydrophobic bonds, mutating but growing our way out of one disaster into another, and meanwhile trapping chaos in our meshes and creating order from it, locking in fats and phospholipids, and blowing micelles up to bubbles that adsorbed more protein and held specific enzymes safely inside them.

One very special bubble, a deceptively simple one, is the red blood cell; and so to the next chapter.

IV

RED CELLS

Think of a phospholipid micelle. It floats around in your plasma as a soft round clump of molecules with all their fatty tails curled and stuck together in the center of it, and all their wettable heads sticking out to face your plasma water. Now blow it up with plasma to make a little balloon of it. You have created a new kind of surface this way: an inner surface, and it is wet like the outside, so it must, like the outside, be faced by phospholipid heads now and no more by tails. Also, plasma proteins are very likely to be adsorbed by both surfaces, and the whole thing will look like this:

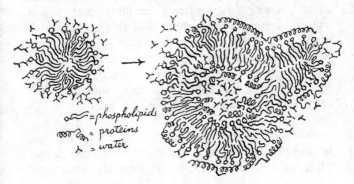

= phospholipids
= proteins
= water

FIGURE 38

That is just about as much of a red cell membrane-like structure as we know. Of course it does not actually form this way. Besides, it may have a double double layer of phospholipid. Also, it cannot be very uniform. If it was, the red cell would be ball-shaped, and the uninterrupted layer of lipid tails would not allow any water to pass through. But the fine structure of the membrane that has become known so far fails to explain how the cell maintains shape, filters water, keeps or pumps sodium out and potassium inside, keeps from sticking to other cells, or keeps its body so soft that it slips through your capillaries almost as easily as liquid does. Microscopists, chemists, immunologists, and rheologists often satisfy themselves with more or less simple models without satisfying each other.

I myself am only a rather baffled bystander. Still, long before I tried to come near a protein molecule, I had approached red cells to within a range of one millimeter. Often, when I was a student in Holland, I would hold a frog's webbed little foot under my microscope, watch the red cells rush by, try to follow one cell in its mad race down a little artery, see it spend a moment at a fork, pick an arteriole, ride slowly down a meandering capillary that would squeeze it from a thick-edged disk into a cylinder, a cone, a hatlike thing, and then . . . relief! on to a wider vessel with room to become a disk again, and off through venules and vein at breakcell speed. A frog, like most amphibia, has large nucleated oval cells. Our own are only about 7.8 microns in diameter.

But soon after I began studying blood in New Brunswick, they began to feel about dime-sized to me. Then, as I became interested in molecular structures,

FIGURE 39

the red cells began to grow again until now they are about seven feet tall and practically audible, but even more mysterious than ever. The electron microscope helps to enlarge both size and mystery. Instead of lenses, it uses circular fields through which electrons fly instead of light. The field forces the electrons to pass through a focal point and through the more transparent parts of your specimen; the specimen thus casts its immense shadow on a screen. Sadly enough, air is not allowed in the electrons' path, so the specimen must be observed in a vacuum, a condition as healthy as being hatless in outer space. All water will have boiled off; only a mummy of the originally juicy slice remains; even then, its density may vary too little from place to place to project a clear picture. There is a very beautiful way of making more visible. It is called metal shadow casting, and goes like this. The slice of tissue, or in our case the slice cut from a preparation of fixed red cells, or even a cast made from a dried preparation, is placed in a vacuum chamber with a little piece of metal suspended like a tiny sun somewhere low over the horizon of your object. The air is pumped out of the chamber, and then the piece of metal is heated, so that it will evaporate, casting its atoms violently around, and hitting your object like a low light, especially anything in it that is elevated, and creating long shadows where the elevated parts protect the object from the "metal rays," like this:

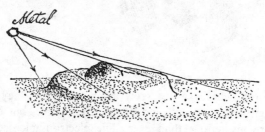

FIGURE 40

Now the shadowed film of matter is put in the electron microscope, where all things coated with metal will be opaque to electrons. That means the sunny side of things will look black, and a negative print has to be made of the view. It will be a picture of a startlingly real landscape, a bird's view of a desert that shows where matter has been left by its water. How horribly the shapes of once live structures have been changed by the utter draught and the tinny glare, no one knows. The dried membrane of a red cell will show plaques this way, and different kinds of plaques for different species. Were they islands of flat micelles, when still alive? Maybe; and maybe their hydrophobic centers could then account for the way some lipid-like molecules can travel through the membrane. It would also be nice if real pores could be seen, or channels, that would let water pass through but not certain ions, or at least not molecules beyond a certain size. But I think that it would be childish to expect any pictures that would support a simple mechanical explanation of membrane functions. Like presuming that the movement of people in and out of their buildings must depend on the size of their doors. We must learn why they have come to any particular door in the first place. The arrangements of atoms along the backbone of each membrane protein molecule, and their relationships with the phospholipid atoms and with the hairs, bristles, webs, and sponges of pure water that form and fall apart ten thousand times each millionth of a second—those are the things we have to see before we can understand exactly how one ion of sodium will tell one story of its adventures in the membrane, and an ion of potassium will tell quite a different one.

Membrane Functions

There are some scientists who feel that the structure of the membrane forces the structure of water to do most of the selective transportation. For example, a row of water molecules, held together almost like a row of paper clips hanging from one magnet, would be able to conduct electrons (i.e., pass a current) easily. Take away the magnet, and the whole chain falls apart into isolated, insolated pieces. Dead wool fibers, say these scientists, are just as able to tell sodium from potassium ions as a "live" membrane is, and besides, they say, a calculation of the amount of energy needed (if indeed it were needed for all membrane functions) right in the membrane seems to give a comically high figure—more energy than can be present in an entire cell. Most other scientists, however, prefer to look at the opposite evidence, that there is a process of selection at work in the membrane and consuming food to stay alive. They feel there is a sodium pump, pumping sodium out of the cell when too much gets in. When you starve red cells by putting them in a solution without glucose, the wrong ions will soon begin to leak in and out. I don't know what all this proves, or who is right; but I think truth could be in the middle. For example, the red cell may need energy for maintenance of the otherwise "dead" membrane. In the molecular world, it becomes a little difficult, and even aimless, to try and tell the living thing from the dead thing it produces.

Even if it is dead, there are clear indications that the membrane is not very simple. Put a drop of fresh blood on a slide, with a small drop of water next to it, and cover with a cover slip and look through the microscope where the two drops have mixed. There you will see the red cells changing—their hollow flanks will begin to bulge with the water the cells are drinking, and some hemoglobin can be seen leaking out until their bodies float around like swollen, round, yet empty balloons. If you had added some salt in time, the cells would have lost much of their excess water and would have recovered their old biconcave shape, and if you then had added more salt, they would have squeezed out even more water, wrinkling and crumpling until they would have looked like spike-covered little balls (Figure 41). Again you can reverse this sickening little disaster by adding the right amount of water: the cells go back to their normal shape. The

after ← adding water   after adding → salt

FIGURE 41

point of this experiment is only that you would see the cell's old shape return not just in general, but in details, and that even the spikes of the shrinking cell would return where they had formed before, each time you repeated the cycle. What would your conclusion be? Others before you have said there must be some invisible structures not only in the membrane, but all through the cell, that force their specific distortions upon the membrane when the cell shrinks.

What makes a red cell, or any cell, move water in from a very watery environment, and out toward a more salty one? The statistics, like those of birth rates, appear dull by erasing any thought of individual cases: the cell "simply" tries to make the total strength of solutions inside it equal to that outside, by moving anything that will pass through its membrane fastest. An old and maybe helpful way of looking at this is by pretending the water is not there. Anything dissolved in it will then seem like a gas, with a gaslike pressure. This is called osmotic pressure; you can also call it tonicity. A solution of 0.85 per cent sodium chloride in water has a rather physiological osmotic pressure, and can be called isotonic with the red cells. In other words, you can keep red cells for a while in this isotonic salt solution; they will not change shape. With less salt—in a hypotonic solution—the cells will swell and burst (lyse), as you saw, and in a hypertonic solution they will shrink and form spikes (crenate). There, now you have it all in scientific terms.

According to an old theory, the tonicity and even the salt composition of our plasma resembles that of seawater, and is, in a way, seawater: as the slimy things we once were began to crawl out of the ocean, and our skins, now bare, hardened against the sun, the air, and the saltless rains, we sealed the seawater dragged out of the sea inside us, and have soaked our cells ever since in a world like the one we left millions of years ago. But why then are our red cells dissatisfied with this world, and insist on collecting more potassium and expulsing sodium ions? Is that proportion of elements essential to the function of red cells? Not at all: dog and cat, for example, have a very low red cell potassium and high red cell sodium, while rat and rabbit have high potassium and low sodium concentrations in their red cells, like we do. Certain sheep have high, and others low red cell potassium. There seems to be some relationship between the sodium:potassium ratio in the cells and the way certain phospholipids are distributed in the membrane. Their function in ion transport is now being studied with artificial membranes. Again the membrane may turn out to be a lifeless expression of life.

Blood Types

Another kind of invisible membrane structure is revealed by blood group studies. You have inherited an everlasting urge to produce certain fatty and sugar-like molecules with each red cell you make, molecules that probably stick with hydrophobic bonds to lipid parts of the cell membrane. For example, you may be blood type O, A, B, or AB, depending on the genes in you that you received from your parents—one from each. A combination of A+A or of A+O makes you type A, B+B or B+O makes you B, A+B makes you AB, and O+O makes you O. Only against the substance you don't make will your body, as your faithful but rather stupid defender, make an antibody that "protects" you against this harmless substance. If completely well-meaning type B cells are infused into a type A person, they will immediately be coated with anti-B protein, survival will become impossible to them, and they will clump and lyse; their dead bodies may well ruin the man's kidneys and his own body too will die, victim of a war that appears typically and humanly senseless.

The A, B, O blood group system, and several others, are too well known and too easily tested to cause such accidents often nowadays. But new ones are still being found. There is a similarity between the discovery of clotting factors or other enzymes, and of blood groups; the most common is discovered last. Let us assume that a Mrs. Xippepaai, when still a mere egg, was hit by a cosmic ray that knocked out a gene present in everyone else and normally responsible for making a certain substance in red cells. Let us call the substance X (short for Xippepaai, named after the only person who does not produce it). Mrs. X grows up and marries a normal man. She becomes pregnant. The embryo does well, and begins to make its own red cells; blessed by its father with a gene to make X substance, it makes normal red cells. Shortly before its birth, a few of these cells or pieces of them find their way through the placenta into the mother's bloodstream. While, so to speak, she gives birth to the normal baby with one hand, she makes antibodies against the substance X on the baby's red cell remnants with the other hand. Some time later the hospital decides for some reason that she needs a bottle of blood to pep her up. She is typed: her red cells clump with serum from type B people, not noticeably with serum from type A people. In a sample from a bottle of nice normal type A blood, a drop of her serum seems to create just a bit of red cell clumping, but it happens to be Monday morning and the technician, unable to see the world in perfect focus, blames his eyes, blesses the bottle, and the transfusion is started. Soon, Mrs. X begins to complain of chills: transfusion reaction! The blood she received acted very much like a booster shot that people are immunized with, and for a while her body is quite busy making anti-X. Thank goodness she does not need any more blood, because now her serum (or plasma) would clump all human red cells in the world but her own. However, she recovers, and two years later she has another baby. This one too seems well when born, but late in the afternoon its skin and the whites of its eyes turn a bit yellow, and it does not seem very active any more. The same technician, who has since given up drinking, comes and takes a sample of blood from the baby. One drop of it he places on a glass slide, touches it to make it spread with another slide, and spreads it elegantly to a thin film like this:

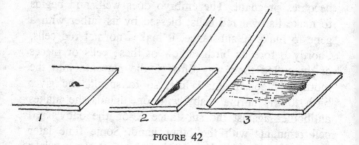

FIGURE 42

The rest of the blood goes in a test tube. Back in the lab, he places the blood smear across a support over a sink and pours a dark purple liquid over it: Wright's stain, a mixture of red acid dye (eosin) and blue alkaline dye (hematoxylin), and alcohol. The alcohol breaks all kinds of physical bonds in the plasma and cell proteins on the slide, so that the proteins become solid and insoluble in the drops of water added next. Now the eosin attaches itself mostly to the alkaline cytoplasm in the cells, and hematoxylin goes mostly to the nucleic acids in the nuclei. The slide is then rinsed and looked at through the microscope. The white cells now look delicately pinkish to lavender, with dark blue to purple nuclei, while the red cells are orangey pink, and sprinkled among the cells there are violet-stippled platelets. But on the smear of this baby's blood the well-prepared technician finds one special kind of cell in very large numbers. It is round like a red cell, and has a round and very dark nucleus. If it has a large nucleus, the cytoplasm looks steel gray. He calls that cell a pronormoblast (Figure 43). If I tell you that a normal

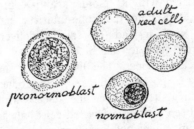

FIGURE 43

red cell is sometimes called a normocyte, and that "blast" comes from a Greek word meaning "sprout," you can guess what the cell is and what it indicates: it is a very young red cell, and its proper place would be in the bone marrow. Then there is a similar-looking kind of cell, looking more like a red cell, its body beginning to turn orange-pink and apparently caught in the act of producing hemoglobin, but still with a small and now almost black little round thing inside: the shrinking nucleus. This cell is a normoblast; the tiny black ball was about ready to pop out of the cell. Meanwhile, back in the test tube, the remaining blood has clotted, the clot has retracted, and the serum it has left around and over it is deep yellow—much too deep yellow.

What has happened to this baby? Like the first one, it has received the gene from its father to make X substance on its red cells. But even before it was conceived, its mother had been immunized against X by the bit of X injected into her by the first baby, and the lot of X injected into her by that transfusion. By the time the second baby in her began to make its red cells, the mother was making anti-X at top speed and was waging an escalating war with her child. Now, almost as fast as the baby can make its red cells, they become coated with its mother's anti-X protein, and break. By this time the bone marrow has become desperate, and instead of calmly delivering well-matured red cells to the bloodstream, it pours out young, nucleated ones. The liver, which should have been ready to go out of the red cell production business, is still at it; and even the spleen, which should only have been making a few red cells half a year ago, is still turning them out half-done. Meanwhile, as the red cells die, their hemoglobin is set free and must be converted into bile pigments: bilirubin for example, which must be accepted by the liver to make bile. But the unmanageable load of yellow stuff piles up in the blood and has turned the plasma into an almost orange liquid.

The doctors are now very worried, and the technician must keep taking blood samples from the baby and report the bilirubin to them. A specialist in the blood bank is standing by: if the reported value reaches a certain mark, he must prepare to exchange the baby's blood for an equal amount of other, problem-free blood if he can find it.

Let us make this a happy and quite reasonable story: the bilirubin levels off, then drops to normal; less and less nucleated red cells are found in the blood smears; the baby perks up; and as mother and child go home, a scientist from the big city comes and offers the mother, now nearly destitute, two hundred dollars for a pint of her blood, which he wants to agglutinate bird cells with.

Usually, it is neither the A, B, O system, nor a rare one like this, but the Rh group system that creates trouble. Rh stands for Rhesus monkey. Leaving out a lot of complications, I will only tell you that you are "Rh-positive" if you produce a substance on your red cells that resembles one made by Rhesus monkeys. You can find this out by injecting Rhesus red cells into some other kind of animal, which will then make antibodies against the Rhesus cells, so that its serum will agglutinate them, but also will agglutinate anything else with "Rhesus substance" on it, like your red cells—if they are "Rh-positive."

There is no reason to be ashamed of sharing a little thing like a blood group substance with a monkey. The craziest animals have been found to contain A substance; there are even plants with something very much like A substance, and others that seem to have something suspiciously like antibodies against A. Among people, more A is made by people from Scandinavia and Australia, more B is produced by Asians. What does all this mean? I have no idea. The substances are rather small molecules; if you throw a handful of sugars, fats, and things together with some kinds of enzymes, maybe the chance is that structures resembling these antigens are easiest or most rapidly formed. If bacteria do this, and if some plants have survived by making real antibodies against them, like we do, all this may be just another demonstration of chemical togetherness.

Well, so much for the red cell's surface, the fantastically mottled bag that recognizes ions, is soft as liquid, yet always returns to the same shape, holds on to small sweet molecules that are typical for its owner, and keeps proteins inside it alive sixty times longer than they could have in the plasma outside. And so we come to the inside of the red cell.

The Formation of Red Cells

At this point I had planned to take you on a trip inside the red cell, but I suddenly realized that all I could reveal would be a well-wrapped pack of conflicting lies. I think it better to tell you how the red cell gets that way, even though we don't know exactly what way it got.

Going back in time through the youth and birth of one cell becomes an endless trip through generations of cells and past the point where the entire, younger and younger child containing them has become a single cell itself, back through the ages of man and ancient mammals until, somewhere in a primeval ocean, a scene of cell birth is most conveniently imagined as if shrouded in the dense mists of the past . . . but they are no more dense than the mists of the present. The formation of a red cell inside one of your bones right now is just as much of a mystery as is the birth of any cell ever born. You can learn to recognize an adult red cell (and even call it a mature erythrocyte) with the microscope in half a minute, and learn to tell a normoblast from certain confusing white cells in about ten minutes, but it should take you days until you can tell a young pronormoblast from a lymphoblast, and it has taken experts a lifetime to give up separating even younger cells. Either the microscope is not good enough as a tool for this, or all blood cells stem from an ancient breed of ancestors lurking in our bones and uniform in all aspects except for chance that stirs them to produce some kind of white cell one week and a litter of pronormoblasts the next. If so, chance itself is the mystery, because it is certainly not blind chance: specific cells are produced as needed. The sick baby, like any adult with healthy bone marrow, reacted to the loss of red cells specifically by making more red cells, and not by making any other cells. Probably, the formation of erythrocytes (erythropoiesis) is stimulated by a specific substance (erythropoietin) that I want to discuss a bit later. First I want to discuss some ways of following the life cycle of an erythrocyte.

The pronormoblast looks more or less like this:

live pronormoblast
(*phase contrast microscope*)

FIGURE 44

There is not much cytoplasm around the nucleus yet, and hemoglobin is just beginning to form. A very complicated relationship between certain DNA molecules of the nucleus and particles containing RNA in the cytoplasm allows a chain of events that ends with hemoglobin formation, so that later, when the nucleus shrivels and breaks down, the production of hemoglobin grinds to a halt. Some ribonucleic acid—protein complexes, forming a weblike structure, will remain for a while and still form hemoglobin. The web can be stained blue with a special dye; a cell like that is called a reticulocyte. If you want to know whether someone is anemic because he has lost blood, or because he fails to make blood, you can make a smear of one drop of his blood that you first mix with this dye, and then count how many out of one thousand of his red cells are reticulocytes. If you find a lot more than say ten of them, the patient probably has a normally reacting bone marrow and must be bleeding somewhere, perhaps internally. There are even cruder, yet also informative measurements you can do; for example, collect some blood from the patient into some calcium-removing substance (like oxalate) or into a trace of heparin (a complex substance from liver) to prevent clotting; place some in a special, heavy-walled, narrow, glass tube on which a scale of 10 cm has been marked off in millimeters. Fill to the 10 cm mark. Centrifuge long and fast, to pack all red cells down. See how far down they go: if to the 40 mark, the blood contains about 40 per cent red cells, or to say it more impressively, the patient's hematocrit is 40 per cent. In another sample, the cells are lysed and the liberated hemoglobin ruined to become a brown liquid by adding acetic acid (vinegar); then the brown-ness of it all is measured as an expression of percentage of hemoglobin originally present in the blood sample. Now you have two values. What new information can you get from their combination? Good.*

You can also actually count how many erythrocytes a certain volume of the patient's blood contains by actually counting them. In principle, that is simple: you take a "red pipette"—a small glass tube with a bulbous part that has a volume about a hundred times as large as the stem part. The thing has marks on it, like this:

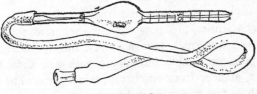

FIGURE 45

Attach a thin aspirating tube of rubber to the pipette, the way I sketched, and suck up the patient's blood to the 0.5 mark. There are tricks to this that you can learn to perform well in a few days' cursing. Wipe tip (another day of frustration) and draw some innocent diluting fluid up in the pipette till the mixture reaches the 101 mark (there goes the rest of your week). Mix awhile; the red bead in the bulb belongs there to help you with this. Now let some drops spill out, quickly wipe the tip again, and let the next drop fill a "counting chamber" (just an expensive piece of glass made to contain a known thickness of liquid and to spread it over a ruled square area), let the cells settle for a while, and count a certain number of

* I presume your new information is: hemoglobin concentration, corrected for presence of plasma.

squares. If you were good, the erythrocytes are nicely and evenly spaced. You know the area you counted, the depth of the chamber, and therefore the volume; and you know the sample was diluted two hundred times, so you can calculate back to find how many red cells there were in a cubic millimeter of the patient's blood. Five and a half million would be about normal for a man of the United States, living at sea level, not under stress; but a good technician has a 10 per cent chance to come up with a count that is, accidentally, close to a million under or over the right one—and not all technicians are good.

Laboratories are now buying expensive machines to rise above such human errors, mostly boxes that accept some sample into one mouth and then hand you a number from another opening, meanwhile hiding their own errors as well as yours. Only by saving time do they indeed give you a greater number of chances to approach truth. Even then, presume you did three red cell counts in a row on one sample of blood, and the values you got were 4.1 million, 4.0 million, and 5.3 million. Must you then pretend that the last one must have been a goof, just because the first two were so close together, or must you take a fourth one to make sure? Many laboratories are not at all strict in their evaluations, or do not even have the time to do anything twice. But presume you are good, and all your mean values are meaningfully near reality. By comparing hematocrit, red cell count and whole blood hemoglobin, you can then find the average red cell volume, and the average hemoglobin content of the average red cell; you may find the patient makes a normal number of cells but with an abnormally low hemoglobin content, or that his cells are abnormally large or small, and see if there are other symptoms to fit a certain disease.

There are more modern and elegant tricks to learn about birth and death of erythrocytes inside a patient, and to find where they come from and where they go. I learned some of these tricks when I began working at Mount Sinai Hospital, before I returned to my own little world of platelets and clotting.

Radioactive Counts

As soon as I came to Mount Sinai, I was introduced to a long, low basement of rooms. Almost all contained big machines, and almost none looked familiar. Shivers of lights running down faces of radiation counters; swiveling dinosaurs with cast-iron heads; "Danger! Radioactive!" signs on doors, cabinets, bottles; and then the technicians. They did usual work in unusual ways: covered the table with wax paper, handled bland-looking bottles with gloves, put any pipette, any test tube with which they had finished immediately in either a basin marked "hot" (for "radioactive") or "cold." The patients too were handled as if more than the usual bit parts was to be expected of them. Awaiting them was a large room with all shades drawn, one or two counting machines slowly clicking, and two dinosaurs, their fat insulated leashes snaked along the floor, flanking a slightly rumpled bed and staring down at the white sheets. Next to the bed a little cart, where servings of syringes, test-tube-loaded chromium racks, and radioactive iron solution were displayed.

The main character in the first performance I was to witness turned out to be a small and kind old lady in

FIGURE 46

a kimono that could not entirely mask the pregnant look of her belly. She entered with the doctor and his assistant talking to her: "You know, dear, that this is going to be an all-day test, and you know what it is all about, don't you?" "All you have to do is lie down on the bed." "We do the rest." "Those two machines will look at that big spleen of yours and at your liver." "To see what that spleen has to do with your cells" "because if you don't need it, for what would you want to walk around with a big thing like that, people would think, you should pardon the expression, at your age, you know, for what?" Strangely enough, when a spleen is very large and producing erythrocytes, it can usually be removed without causing a bad drop in total red cell production. Still, it was important to find out what exactly birth and death of red cells was like in this patient. Here is how that was done.

The old lady received a certain amount of radioactive iron (Fe^{59})—not just as a solution, because free iron would just creep through all kinds of interfaces, including those of the blood vessel walls, and it would get lost unless it could attach itself in time to a special protein in the plasma, called transferrin. Stuck to the big transferrin, iron would come along peacefully. Therefore, before the radioactive iron was injected, it was incubated with a solution of purified transferrin. Meanwhile, the lady had gone to bed, where one dinosaur got its radiosensitive head pressed against her spleen while the other one was seriously sniffing her liver. The counters, to which each monster was connected, were slowly counting the "background": the slight radioactivity mostly caused by cosmic rays that hit all of us eternally out of far outer space.

Now some blood was taken from a vein in the lady's left arm, and the needle, remaining in the vein, was stoppered and taped to her skin: it must not slip out. Into her right arm, the radioactive iron, now attached to transferrin, was injected. Then more blood was taken via that needle in the left arm, and again half a minute later, and again and again at longer and longer intervals. The samples, marked "30 seconds", "1", "2", "4" minutes and so on, were centrifuged and 1 ml of plasma from each was placed in a kind of miniature well of thick lead. A sensitive bottom in the well, protected by the lead from radioactive noise of the outside world, then measured the activity of the plasma. The first plasma samples were quite "hot": the machine, set to count something like 10240 counts and then to stop and show how long it took getting to that point, polished the first samples off in minutes. Plasma samples taken about two hours later would only make the counter click, click, very slowly and long: almost all radioactive iron had left the lady's plasma. Her red cells too were "cold." But the dinosaur sniffing her spleen had become very excited: its counter was ticking away madly, telling us that much radioactive iron had gone to her spleen.

Meanwhile, in another room, some of the lady's before-iron-injection blood sample had been put in a small sterile bottle with sterile sodium chromate of which the chromium atom was radioactive. The red cells had immediately started tagging themselves by drinking the radioactive chromium. After several manipulations to stop the tagging and to measure the activity of a small sample from the tagged cells, the rest was returned to the lady by injecting them into her right arm, and a while later, samples were taken from her left arm. You can guess what item of information we could get from those samples plus a few tests you already know.

Once you know the lady's hematocrit, the hematocrit of the injected sample (which is diluted with some salt solution that was used to wash excess radioactive chromium off the cells), the radioactivity of the injected sample, and the radioactivity of the mixture of the lady's own, "cold" red cells that had never left her body before and were never tagged but that had been stirred inside her with the "hot" red cells that were injected—with all that information available, you can calculate what per cent the known amount of hot cells occupies among the cold cells, and how large the total red cell volume and the total blood volume of the lady are. A much cleaner method than that of a few hundred years ago, when all blood had to be removed to get some rough idea.

Well, by the time all these samples had been taken, the day was about gone, and our lady was exhausted. The next day, and the next several days, and then once a week, blood samples were taken and their radioactivity was measured. But now a complication arises: the lady contained two tags, iron and chromium. How tell them apart? Nowadays a filter is used that helps screening out pulses from one source while passing those from the other; you simply do one count with and one without the filter and compare. But in those days, we had to use a different trick. If you just keep a radioactive element, you will find that it spends its activity at a very constant rate-decreasing rate, or, to say it more neatly, each element has a specific half-life, which is the time wherein half of its activity disappears. It always takes that time, no matter how much the "whole" is you start with. Therefore we could just do this: measure the activity of the sample now, and again a certain number of days later, then ask our mathematician to apply a set of equations and known half-life values to the two counts, and up would pop the two values, one for amount of radioactive iron, and the other for radioactive chromium in the red cells. This way we found out that on the day after injection, our patient had not brought any of the iron into circulation, but one or two days later, the first iron-tagged red cells began to appear in her blood, then many more showed up, while ever since the first day, the chromium tag dropped. The iron count soon reached its peak and then also began to drop slowly. What does all this mean to you?

It means, for one thing, that the lady's spleen could make red cells, starting from raw iron (and other, un-tagged material, of course), in about two to three days. So, by the way, can your bone marrow. The continuously dropping chromium means that some of this tag disappeared from circulation immediately, and that in turn means that either it has dropped off the red cells that were injected, or the cells themselves have died.

No wonder: the sample of her blood that we tagged in that bottle of chromium salt must have represented a random sample of all ages of her red cells. Some she must have freshly made, but others may already have been ready to die when we captured them; then when we returned them, they did die. Corrections for this error can be made, and one other correction is needed: the radioactivity of the tag element gets weaker as time passes, and as you remember.

Well, the story of our lady ended well, or rather, it went on—maybe thanks to some of our test results—after her spleen had been removed. I think the over-ambitious organ was destroying more red cells than it made, and shortened her red cell survival time.

Hemoglobin and Red Cell Survival Time

Normally, in you, erythrocytes will live about 120 days. You can also say it this way: every four months I have renewed all of my red cells. Or (I calculated, and please check me): every second I must make— and kill—two million of them. A good thing we have only about a thousand times fewer white cells than red cells, because most of our white cells live only about a week. And every free protein molecule in our plasma, on the average, lives only for a few mad days. Yet, when a red cell has matured and stops making hemoglobin, it lives another 115 days more and so does its hemoglobin. There must be a healthy atmosphere for proteins inside the red cell. Several enzymes must be working to keep its membrane intact. There is also one, called methemoglobin reductase, that will re-move oxygen from hemoglobin when it accidentally binds the oxygen atom chemically instead of just lightly enough to pass it on when tissues ask for it. You could say that the hemoglobin burns itself a bit sometimes, and has to be healed, but it suffers a bit each time and eventually it will die.

Mechanically speaking, life in the erythrocyte cannot be very quiet at all: most of the time the cell has to make its complete rounds: heart—big lung artery—lung capillaries (squeeze, take up oxygen, give off carbon dioxide)—vein—heart (get hit by valves, maybe)—aorta (rush)—smaller vessels—capillaries somewhere (squeeze, take up carbon dioxide, give off oxygen), all in about twenty-three seconds. (Incidentally, if you are a rabbit, the time is only 7½ seconds, but almost no matter what mammal you are, it will take you about twenty-seven heartbeats to drive your blood fully around; also, the smaller you are, the shorter your red cells live, in general, so maybe an erythrocyte can stand only a more-or-less fixed number of cycles or heartbeats.) Chemically too, life in the erythrocyte is far from asleep. I must confess that I am just not good enough in this field to assemble all information about the shifts that take place when oxygen is taken up or released. If you want to read something about it at all, begin with the article "The hemoglobin molecule" by M. F. Perutz in *Scientific American*, November 1964, pages 64 to 76. His work, combined with earlier and later literature, gives me the impression that this is what happens:

Let us say the one particular red cell we are watching is approaching a lung. Now it is being squeezed into a sausage, through a lung capillary. Watch any one of the cell's hemoglobin molecules that happens to be closest to the cell membrane and therefore closest to the lung air. (And look at Figure 34 on page 88 if you need it.) One disk of heme on an alpha chain (remember there are four chains: two alpha, two beta, each with a heme disk) happens to be the first one hit by an oxygen atom. Immediately, somewhere near it, a water molecule that had been forming a delicate bridge with its two bonding hydrogen atoms, breaks loose, and a second heme catches an oxygen atom. Still the hemoglobin molecule has not changed its shape noticeably, though it turned a bit brighter red; but there, a third heme, this time even more rapidly, is found by an oxygen atom, and suddenly the two beta chains are moved slightly apart —helped by the alpha chains—and the fourth heme has somehow become a few hundred times more available to another oxygen atom, which comes over to be embraced. Meanwhile the molecule has not been sitting still. The contortions of the erythrocyte during its rough ride, as well as the continuous dither so typical for all warm molecules, is carrying our fellow deeper into the cell where it meets its less oxygenated fellows, and some quick exchange takes place. This way, though the tangle of red protein molecules is so dense that it looks almost like a solid crystal, the oxygen atoms are being carried through more rapidly than if they had met mere water.

Meanwhile, the hemoglobin has also released carbon dioxide, and this has combined with a molecule of red cell water. Complicated reactions probably result, ions go back and forth through the membrane, and a sodium atom outside the cell, where it had been either kept or thrown by the membrane, catches the carbon dioxide chemically. The carbon dioxide molecule that finally goes into the lung space may not be the same one that came off the hemoglobin. Now the cell is relaxing into its disk shape and picking up speed as it passes through wider and wider vessels; one vortex and another one, and it has gone safely through the heart and down, until it slows down into a capillary of the left thumb skin. Again watch a hemoglobin molecule nearest the membrane, where it almost seems to touch the capillary wall and the oxygen-poorer world beyond. It gives off one oxygen atom, and immediately the two beta chains approach each other, somehow making it easy for the next oxygen to break off its heme pad. Carbon dioxide is taken up, and so on, and so on.

Somehow, after about three hundred thousand cycles of this, things in the cell have turned old, too old. Some water got lost: the cell is heavier. Chemically, the face of the membrane has changed. Inside, many things may have gone wrong. Too many hemoglobin molecules may have been burning themselves on the oxygen and turned into methemoglobin, and minute changes in the control mechanism, maybe in the shape of the protecting methemoglobin reductase, are slowing down first aid. The membrane becomes more and more tender, and finally it yields: pores open all over it, and it sweats hemoglobin as it dies. Released into the plasma, each hemoglobin molecule enjoys only brief liberty; then it is grabbed by a haptoglobin molecule and attacked by many enzymes. The alpha and beta chains are snapped into pieces, and the pieces are broken into single amino acids. The four hemes, each looking like a little flat flower, are turned into four little strings of petals exhibiting spectacular colors: bile pigments, to be used by the liver for bile. Out of each heme, the little heart of iron is picked by transferrin and taken back to the bone marrow for reincarnation in a new cell.

You must know from certain advertisements that not all iron returns. You lose some, because once in

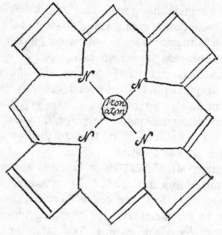

FIGURE 47

a while you have to eat some molecules that contain iron in a useful form. If, obviously, your iron does not merely trot around a blind four-month circle within you but often goes astray, it (or any other part of the red cell that will be even less tractable) cannot serve as a messenger to the bone marrow, announcing the need for replacing a hemoglobin molecule that has just died. A stupid system like that would not work anyway: whenever some accident caused you to lose some blood, your locked-up marrow would never receive the news, with its messengers dying outside you. You cannot operate as a closed system; the world would not let you live unprepared for itself. If oxygen transport is the most important function of your red cells and their hemoglobin, then the demand for more red cells that the world may sometimes impose on you must actually be a demand for more oxygen transport facilities, and any tissue that would find itself short of

oxygen could be a good alarmist if it would only produce some substance when needed to stimulate the
bone marrow with, some hormone. And indeed it appears that the kidney is such a tissue, and that, when
short of oxygen, it produces a substance called erythropoietin. When your body has to work harder for a
while, or when you move to high mountains in thin
air, or when your heart slows down more than it
should, more erythropoietin is made by your kidneys,
and soon more reticulocytes appear in your blood,
and your red cell count increases until your kidneys
are happy again.

This is probably only part of the system that de-
termines the number of erythrocytes to be allowed in
circulation. One or more substances seem to control
the release of new cells already made; certain experiments even indicate that the brain can make the flow
of reticulocytes out of the marrow stop or go.

The whole complex suggests that to remain alive
certain things inside you must remain constant, and
they may demand other things to fight for this peace,
just as it seems to be the fate of soldiers abroad that
they must go from battle to boredom to battle to keep
the life of those at home as monotonous as ever. We
must be full of systems like that; negative feedback
systems they could be called. Less oxygen—more
erythropoietin—more red cells—more oxygen—less
erythropoietin. Standing up but leaning too far forward—reflex via your spinal column to make you lean
back—too far back—reflex to make you lean forward.
And there you stand, proudly constant, you hope.
When you speak too softly your displeased brain
makes you speak more loudly, at all times demanding
you speak your own way; the way it lets you write
tomorrow must be recognized as the way you wrote

today. Frankly, what essentials survive by constancy
I do not know. Man I agree would probably not propagate the usual way if his mate were unable to maintain
some recognizable shape for more than a few minutes,
but even there what is essential shape we do not
know.

If we believe that anything more constant is also
more essential, then it may be rewarding to look for
constant relationships of measurements among various species. For example, the red cell count of goats
is about eighteen million per cubic millimeter, while
yours is about five million, but the size of the goat's
erythrocytes is so much smaller than yours, that you
both have about the same hematocrit; packed together, the red cells take roughly 30 per cent of all
blood space in the goat and 40 per cent in you. Most
mammals have a hematocrit in that range, so if you
believe in constants more than in variables, you will
feel that it was more important for mammals to have
a certain hematocrit than to have any particular size
of red cell, even if one species eventually did stick to
one size. In that case, how about the following facts:
red cell diameter varies more among species than red
cell thickness; and the amount of hemoglobin per red
cell varies a lot more than the concentration of hemoglobin in red cells among species. The latter fact plus
the constancy of hematocrits tell you that all species
have about the same amount of hemoglobin per volume of whole blood. But the fact that all red cells
have about the same concentration of hemoglobin
should be no more amazing than that an egg box contains exactly twelve eggs: they cannot be packed
tighter and be safe. Perhaps a hematocrit of more than
50 per cent leads to trouble, such as too high a viscosity for the heart to pump around; the poor little muta-

tions born with kidneys and bone marrow insisting on such a useless level simply died childless.

The thickness of red cells may be more constant than the diameter because the phospholipids and proteins and cholesterol mixture forming the membrane just cannot bend sharply enough to make flatter cells. I am sure that at least certain body shapes do not vary widely among beasts because they must contain a certain kind of molecule, and that it is the limitations of that sort of molecule's shape and size beyond which it cannot be useful, which dictate how round or flat and how large the structure can be that carries it.

This brings us back to page 57, and the question: Does the structure of hemoglobin (for example) have to be that way? Does its shape dictate what vehicle it needs: erythrocytes; and is its shape in turn dictated by the way heme must be held? It is very interesting that our muscles contain a red pigment called myoglobin that is shaped exactly like the beta chain of hemoglobin; it is even more interesting that odd organisms here and there have produced hemoglobin, while others made other oxygen-capturing pigments, but only those—like a worm called Thalassema—which produced hemoglobin may also make red cells to put the hemoglobin in. So maybe the molecule indeed dictates what vehicle it shall have.

Looking back, you cannot easily imagine an animal as active as we are, living without red cells that protect our hemoglobin. There are icefish living in the Antarctic at less than 2 degrees Centigrade, and just lying around with their large mouth open to gulp the abundant food. They have no red cells and no hemoglobin at all, and their bodies look white. The oxygen simply physically dissolved in their plasma is all they need. We the people would need sixty times more plasma than we have to hold the oxygen now held by our red cells. But then we would weigh three hundred pounds more. But then, as someone has calculated, we would need three times more oxygen to drag this liquid around. But then . . . how good it is to have red cells.

V

WHITE CELLS

When a very thin slice of artificially hardened blood has gone through all our usual destructive treatments intended to preserve it and to make its details visible, electron microscope photographs of it will show the red cells as large, dark, and dreary islands, like stiffened puddles of asphalt in a desert. Platelets sprinkled about will then be as pretty as flowers. And for every five hundred red cells or so, there will be a leukocyte (white cell) as beautiful as a garden filled with patterns of lacy little things (Figure 48). Even on a primitive blood smear, stained the way I described (see page 106), and seen through a simple microscope, the uncut white cells stand out, blossoming in the dull field of red clay-colored pancaked erythrocytes (Figure 48).

There are five types of white cells easily distinguishable on such a blood smear (Figure 49). Three of them appear members of one family—the *granulocytes* —because their cytoplasm (everything inside but the nucleus) looks as grainy as farina or even rice would look if enlarged one time instead of one thousand times, as these cells are. If their cytoplasm has stained itself like a grayish purple farina, the cells are called *neutrophils:* the color is a rather neutral mixture of

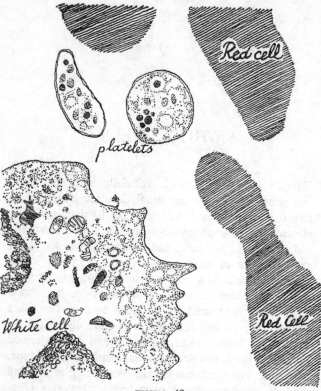

FIGURE 48

the basic blue and the acid red component of the dye. If, however, the cytoplasm contains big granules stained orange with the red component (the eosin), the cells are called *eosinophils*. And if they contain large granules stained blue-black, the cells are called *basophils*. All of the granulocytes, at least when adult, have oddly shaped nuclei, especially the neutrophil ones; they are also called polymorphonuclear, for that reason.

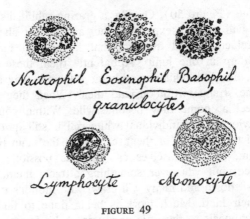

FIGURE 49

Then there are *lymphocytes,* with rather round, dark nuclei, and an occasional *monocyte,* more transparent and foamy looking. If the smear has been well made, all these normal white cells will appear neatly separated and as round and flat as painted paper plates. Don't let them fool you. In a drop of fresh blood, the phase microscope will show a granulocyte, for example, tumbling around like a glass marble at first, but after a while it will squat down on the glass. As if relaxing at last, it will start feeling around: a clear blister will swell out of its rim, some cytoplasm that seems to have turned watery will fill it with wildly dancing specks that slow down again as if the liquid around them is turning thick and fleshy. Another blister will form, maybe extending the first one, and so on, making the whole cell flow out long and narrow, pulling the oddly permissive, lumpy nucleus out into a blobbed string. Then the granulocyte may suddenly decide to become round again, as if startled by something it sniffed, contracting in such a hurry that it leaves a sloppy trail of smeared-out cytoplasmic tail behind (Figure 50). Or, like a grazing rabbit, its front part will seem to explore farther and farther ahead of its reluctant hind quarters that finally will have to catch up in one jump. Apparently then, these white cells, like little children, only sit still until they adjust to the strange world around them. When they begin to feel at home they become wild. Within you, the behavior of any individual white cell is still quite unpredictable. Many of them, carried in the main bloodstream, hold themselves as small as possible: ball-shaped; but whenever something attracts them, they will sit down and many will crawl with motions typical of their kind. Much work is being done to find out what appeals to the little creatures. A bit later I hope to tell you something about their very sophisticated tastes.

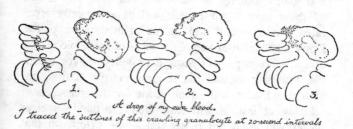

A drop of my own blood.
I traced the outlines of this crawling granulocyte at 20-second intervals

FIGURE 50

One thing I believe is most important to me right now: that the white cell we look at, like the protein molecule that we cannot even see, will act according to whatever we give it to act upon or whatever acts upon it. We must put it in the light, on a slab of glass or plastic, and often, in the crudest error of all, we must kill it to have an even better look at this form of life. The beauty of a cell that had its entrails curdled with alcohol and coated with red and blue dyes—like all beauty—is a product of hidden laws. As from a good product of art, enough of the real truth has been omitted to leave a skeleton so bare that we are able to admire it, and so simple that it allows us to imagine we understand. I have found myself tainted with the most ridiculous prejudices. For example, I cannot help feeling that the granules of a basophil, because they stain so black and chunkily, must be almost as hard as pebbles. And the granules of an eosinophil, stained orange with eosin, look so much like rock candy that I must force myself to remember they are not acid. If we could only get closer and closer to a drop of living blood—and necessarily get smaller and smaller as we went—how long would it then maintain its first so obvious properties? Its shape disappears as we enter, its color fades to a pale yellow, and then becomes deeper again as the light from outside is filtered through more and more red cells around us, and as we become smaller yet, even its wetness disappears into empty space as we slip between its molecules of water. By then even the walls of red and white cells are no longer rigid, but open up like bead curtains, to show us that the old reality of things so solidly segregated when seen from afar, has dissolved and was never more than a clumsy time exposure of a wild and intricate dance. It is bad enough that we cannot see small enough; it is worse that we cannot see briefly enough. If we could see one million times one million times faster, we could see that the water is made up of always forming and breaking clusters, but our slow senses only give us an unchanging, smudged image, a statistical, dead average for our slow, long-living mind. One minute in a uniformly moist, white fog to us, may be a year-long series of floods interrupted by many dry spells to a tiny, fast, and briefly living bug.

With this long paragraph, I hope I have prepared you and myself for one very flagrant mystery that I have not even mentioned in the red cell chapter: How do the newly formed cells leave their place of birth—which is not the blood—and enter the blood that is in a completely closed system? Once in the blood, the red cells stay there till dead, and even most protein molecules probably do not pass through the blood vessel walls. But the tremendous body of a neutrophil slips through without leaving a trace of a leak. I can only bring myself to believe a plain fact like that if I imagine seeing it very close by, as some very rapid and reversible rearrangement. For example, I can think that multimolecular films of the blood vessel membrane change when the white cell membrane touches them, that some outer fringe of long molecules stands up on both, that the bead curtain of the vessel wall spreads along the surface of the white cell, and that the wall seals itself around the cell that it sucks through; and that, once through, the cell rearranges the beads of its own outer curtain to expel or ingest the remaining film of blood vessel wall around it, as the cell pulls itself off the outside of the wall.

Actually, almost nothing is known about the white cell membrane. On the other hand, its cytoplasm is so much more bulky and contains so many beautifully defined structures, that it has been analyzed much more elaborately. Substances, especially enzymes, have been found that seem to express the general and special activities in which the cells differ from each other, but the arrangement of these enzymes and their activity distribution in space is only beginning to be known, and mostly they are still like verbs picked randomly

out of context—we know the action, but not where or
why it is.

I must not give you the impression that only the
invisibly small detail can give us information about
the cells' functions. Just plain old counts to find what
cells appear when and where should tell us at least
something; here is a brief description of how these
counts are usually done.

White Cell Counts

The problem in counting white cells is that there
are normally five hundred to one thousand times more
red cells. Luckily, these lyse (see page 107) more easily than white cells under the right conditions, so if you
will look back (page 116) to see how red blood cells
were counted, you can think of some simple tricks to
make white cell counting equally easy.

As you may have guessed, you draw a drop of blood
into a special white cell pipette up to a certain mark,
and then fill the remaining marked space up with a
solution (usually something that smells like vinegar
because it practically is vinegar) that lyses the red
cells and dilutes the sample only about twenty times
instead of two hundred times, as in the red cell pipette.
You already know how a chamber is filled; usually a
much larger area in it is needed for counting the rather
widely separated white cells. Soon, I hope, this very
primitive method, that is allowed to give values 20
per cent too high or too low, will have become a museum scene. There are now electronic counters that
can swallow a large volume of cell suspension and pass
it through a tiny hole to record every single cell coming
by. Either way, you will then get the total white cell

count of about five thousand to ten thousand per cubic millimeter of blood, normally.

For a so-called CBC (complete blood count) you need more than the hematocrit, total red cell and total white cell count. You also want to differentiate between different types of white cells, and for that information you need stained blood smears (see page 110). The smear is "read" by passing it slowly up, down, and sideways in the microscope, and listing every white cell seen, for example by pushing the buttons on a row of counters, each counter representing a type of white cell. Such a gadget is usually made to ring a bell when the total of cells counted is one hundred, because at that moment each counter represents the percentage out of all white cells that were of its type. This way, if you are a normal adult who is fairly relaxed and has no worms, you will be found to have about 55 per cent to 60 per cent adult granulocytes, neutrophil, 25 per cent to 35 per cent lymphocytes of assorted sizes, roughly 5 per cent monocytes, 2 per cent eosinophils and less than 1 per cent basophils. Obviously, to get any meaningful figure for these latter two, more than one hundred, and perhaps more than ten thousand white cells would have to be counted, so techniques have been developed to count these cells directly, in a chamber, by staining them and destroying all other white cells.

The large percentage of neutrophil granulocytes and of lymphocytes usually seen on a smear makes it possible to count even more differentially and give percentages of younger and older cells. Each type is usually born in its own world: the granulocyte in the bone marrow, the lymphocyte in lymph glands, the monocyte in a kind of tissue called the reticulo-endothelial system that grows as patches in liver, spleen, and other marsh-like scenery. Wherever they are born, the white cells must come from "primitive" forms, large cells usually, with large round nuclei. Somehow these stem cells must remain young, yet the cells they form by dividing will divide several times themselves and become each time more and more like the adult ones that have entered the blood. In 1904, Arneth published a diagram of granulocytes with the youngest form shown at the left, and older and older forms to the right (see Figure 51). Since then, a differential count

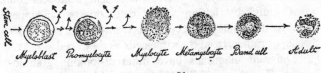

FIGURE 51

with more than the normal percentage of young cells is said to show a "shift to the left." It shows that cells have been formed and pushed out into the bloodstream in a hurry, and suggests that whatever is wrong with the patient may perhaps demand more of this kind of cell, or that something in his sick body makes him form some substance that stimulates the stem cells to production, or that destroys the old cells, or anything else you may think of.

Luckily, some specific cell types have led to occasionally more specific ideas than the ones I just gave you.

Granulocytes: Neutrophils, Eosinophils, Basophils

The steps from stem cell to adult *neutrophil* have been counted. The stem cell splits once to form one myeloblast; the myeloblast splits and each of the two new cells splits to make a total of four promyelocytes; each of those splits twice to make sets of four myelocytes; three hours later each myelocyte has become a metamyelocyte; nine hours later each metamyelocyte has transformed itself into a band cell named after its now band-shaped nucleus; and a day later the band has become the oddly knobbed thing that makes us recognize the cell as an adult neutrophil, on its way to the bloodstream, though it usually seems to take another three days to arrive there. The time schedule was found by letting young cells take up isotopes that could then be recovered from older and older cells, or rather, from the same cells as they aged.

Different mammals have different-looking granulocytes. The neutrophils of rats often have snaky and almost ring-shaped nuclei, while those of rabbits and guinea pigs have granules that stain reddish with eosin and are called "pseudo-eosinophils."

The final three long days before the completed cell pops out of the marrow into the blood may be, to use missile language, a final hold in the countdown with all the cell's systems "go" and waiting for some final command that in turn depends on the demand for more cells in the blood. In dogs, at one session, seven times the amount of white cells circulating at one time can be removed, so that the bone marrow must have had a reserve of at least seven times as many white cells as were circulating—but the term "circulating" is a bit tricky. Probably about half the granulocytes in your blood at any instant are sitting a few round trips out against your blood vessel walls, for example now, while you are relaxed and reading. Under stress, these cells may swarm off the surface and back in the stream. Normally they seem to spend only about ten hours in your blood anyway, and then walk off through the walls in their mysterious way. This means that you must receive an entirely new set of granulocytes more than twice daily, statistically speaking: their walk-offs are of course not likely to be as synchronized as workers' day and night shifts. I think it surprising and rather endearing of these cells to wait so much longer for their trip than their actual trip will last.

Where do they go, after their short visit to the blood? Their bodies are recovered in the lungs, and pieces land in liver and spleen without leaving a clear trail of their brief adventures. Most likely, they will have migrated after a distant call, some substance liberated by an infected wound, perhaps. If the substance called long enough, they may have searched for its origin by aiming for its highest intensity; then, reaching the battlefield, they will have attacked the source and swallowed it: live bacteria, dead and decaying chunks of tissue, anything coated with a specially appetizing layer of specific proteins, as you will see near the end of this chapter. During and after its meal, the cell will have used many of its enzymes: proteases to digest proteins, lipase to digest fats, but also other enzymes to burn the fuel that keeps their physical systems working, their finger-like pseudopods forming, embracing, engulfing. Work is needed to repair its membrane, because its flabby fingers that grab their victim also grab each other and must find their own folds engulfed along with their prey. As the meal goes on beyond endurance, the neutrophil granulocyte that has finally eaten itself sick will begin to let go of its granular cytoplasm in little pieces before it dies, and the little pieces floating around may be eaten in turn by lymphocytes arriving later. Here, right at the infection site, and in the spleen and other places where more pieces of granulocyte arrive, a change will come over the lymphocytes and young plasma cells. They will be stimulated by the foreign particles in this dying granulocyte flesh when they eat it . . . but more about that in the section on lymphocytes. You may skip there if you want to, but just to keep the granulocyte family intact, I have to go on with its other two members.

How rare are *eosinophils?* I would be too typically the popular science writer if I grimly insisted that figures are fun, and then proceeded to try and play with them myself, forgetting all about you. Figure out for yourself, if you want, what it means that only 2 per cent of your white cells are eosinophils. How many is that per cubic millimeter? How far apart from each other are they distributed within your blood? How many do you own all together?

To count eosinophils really, you have to make them stand out. This is done with a solution that contains a dye to stain them, alkali to break up all other white cells, and a highly light refractile substance to make the red cells less visible, just as glass is less visible in water than in air. With this mixture and a white cell pipette you dilute a drop of blood tenfold, fill a counting chamber, and count cells over a very large surface area. The method has been good enough to discover, for example, that as you get up in the morning the number of eosinophils in your blood will reach their lowest point for the day. Some (in contrast to others) believe the drop does not occur in blind people and is caused by some effect of light on a certain area in the retina. One important event definitely known to depress the number of circulating eosinophils takes place in the bottom of your brain: there, your pituitary gland produces ACTH (adrenocorticotropic hormone). It forces the outer layers of your adrenals to produce cortisone-like hormones, and these, somehow, cause your circulating eosinophils to get lost. To test your adrenals' responsiveness, your doctor can have an eosinophil count done on you, then inject ACTH and see if the next count will be lower. Many things that happen to you during stress, be it fright, flight, fun, or fight, are caused by your production of ACTH, though I cannot possibly tell you if the destruction of your eosinophils will add to your fun or if it will at least help you to survive it.

As a matter of fact, all this tells you nothing about the function of these cells. I can give you a bit more information that is almost just as helpful. For example, the following can cause a huge increase in circulating eosinophils: allergic reactions such as asthma, injection of heparin, of histamine, of parasitic roundworm (Ascaris) extract, and of asbestos. In allergic reactions, the eosinophils apparently migrate to areas where the antigen is reacting most with antibodies. There may be logical connections between all these findings: adrenal cortical hormones suppress allergic reactions as well as a number of eosinophils. And about asbestos: often, solutions are filtered in the lab to make them sterile and suitable for injection. The pads used as filters often contain asbestos, and have been found to shed occasional fibers into solutions, causing an outbreak of eosinophils in the recipient for which the dissolved substances have been falsely accused. What intrigues me about this is that eosinophils were also found to have a great appetite for a more natural fiber: fibrin. The effects of heparin and histamine are also intriguing: these are two substances that occur in basophils, and it was found that where basophils break down, eosinophils are likely to appear.

No matter how conspicuous the *basophils* look, with their granules staining as dark as thunder, a good direct method for counting these really rather rare cells has only been invented quite recently. Separating them is even harder, of course, so it is no wonder that very little is known about them. There is a kind of cell in your tissues that is called a mast cell. Mast cells can be collected nicely and studied, but no one knows if they are identical or at least comparable with the blood basophils. Both, like the eosinophils, do decrease under stress, in the morning, and with adrenal corticosteroids, or at least they seem to decrease, but they may in reality only become invisible on staining because they lose their granules. As I said, the granules probably liberate their heparin and histamine, and thus lure the eosinophils. The eosinophil granules, in turn, also seem to affect the basophils, so you can build several possible sequences out of this.

The frustrating thing about basophils is that they contain and obviously liberate such important and well-known substances without telling us why they do. Histamine affects your capillaries, certain intestinal activities, and can give you a headache even without studying it. Heparin not only inhibits blood clotting in several ways, but also makes a lipase (fat-splitting enzyme) out of an inactive plasma protein. The fatty acids, split off fat particles by the enzyme, would be dangerous and lyse red cells because they are detergents, but albumin will pick them up quickly.

I read that there are still twenty-five theories about the function of basophils. Maybe you can now make your own, twenty-sixth.

Lymphocytes, Plasma Cells, and Immunity

The impression I get from present literature is that a parent of lymphocytes will divide once to make a lymphoblast that will divide, and three more divisions will create a group of large lymphocytes; two divisions of each large lymphocyte will create four medium-size lymphocytes, and these again will each form a batch of small lymphocytes (Figure 52). All this happens

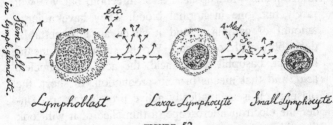

FIGURE 52

in lymph nodes, the spleen, and other places, probably including the bone marrow. The cells pour through the lymph ducts into the blood at a rate that would be enough for several complete refills a day, giving the impression that the blood must consume them at an unbelievably fast rate—but it now appears that many lymphocytes sneak back into the lymph after circulating with the blood. Such a more or less 8-shaped traffic pattern does explain why scientists looking at only part of it have been estimating the life of a lymphocyte to last either a few hours or a few months, but it does not tell where the lymphocytes eventually go.

Almost certainly, lymphocytes do make antibodies,

but they may not go to the extremes that plasma cells
go to. Plasma cells (Figure 53) grow up in the bone

FIGURE 53

marrow and wind up at sites of infection, but you will
rarely find one in normal blood. They have a large
amount of cytoplasm and it stains an unforgettable,
deep blue with our usual Wright stain. Blue means
basophil, basophil means acid, the acid is ribonucleic
acid, and that means protein production. In short, the
plasma cell is a fanatically active protein factory. Under the electron microscope, a thin slice of it will look
like this:

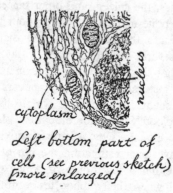

Left bottom part of
cell (see previous sketch)
[more enlarged]

FIGURE 54

You see a section of what must have been a series of shells within shells of shelves carrying particles that contain the necessary enzymes lined up like bottles in the closet of a chemistry lab—only in the cell the chemicals may be mostly on the outer surface of the bottles.

Well, there they sit. What sets them to work, and to work against what? Probably we can say that the first step is up to the cell itself, and to its outer membrane: the foreign matter to be fought must first be eaten by the cell so that it can have a closer look at it. What it eats may originally have been a piece of dying granulocyte, still containing its food that will now act as a dissolving antigen and will affect the plasma cell or the lymphocyte that ate it, very profoundly. Lymphocytes may be completely transformed into large, young-looking cells by the experience.

The next step for the cell is to recognize the dangerous substance as foreign, by some outstanding features of it. These features must be rather rigid, because the antibody to be built against it must be a sharply fitting likeness: a blurred photograph looks like too many people. Molecules with stiff rings of six carbon atoms are good posers, but long, wriggling chains, like high-saturated fatty acids, are not, and no good antibodies are made against them. Also, any small molecule, to become antigenic (and to be called a "hapten") must become attached to a protein. Of course, entire pure proteins can also be antigenic.

Now, how does the plasma cell or lymphocyte recognize the substance as foreign, or, to say this more amazingly and correctly: How does it recognize the thousands of proteins that are your own as non-foreign? Perhaps the thymus has something to do with this. The thymus is a pale, flabby thing that sits in your chest, where it has been shrinking ever since you were about ten years old. It probably stimulates your plasma cells and lymphocytes even now to make antibodies. In very young mammals, foreign proteins can be injected without causing antibody formation. The thymus is then still very small and perhaps does not yet stimulate the process. Anything the animal has or receives at that time will have been and will still be permanently recorded as "me." Even later, when thymus and the alert antibody formation have grown, and even much later, when the thymus is shrinking again, that same protein injected then can be injected again —it will be remembered and need not fear to be attacked. Of course this does not reduce the mystery, and only gives it a time schedule, but it seems reasonable that we must all acquire a tolerance of our "selves," and that, as embryos, we will just have to accept all new proteins that keep sprouting in us until our bodies are old enough to know what they want. From then on, nothing new is regarded as friendly any more, and even the most innocent substances, as all hay fever sufferers and others with allergies know, are attacked with a quite ridiculous fury. Even the protein of your own eye lens, since it has formed in isolation, unseen by your blood, and has never shown itself to your antibody-forming cells, will become an antigen to them if it ever leaves its seclusion. For example, when injected into your blood it will make you form antibody against your own lens.

At present, many diseases are regarded as autoimmune diseases. The patient suffering from any such disease must somehow suddenly have failed to recognize a protein as his own, and in his effort to kill it he kills himself. Possibly the protein is sometimes to blame—it may have become distorted or have broken out of its isolation, but just as likely it is the memory in the plasma cell- or lymphocyte-producing system that can fail.

The word "memory" is being used for a deeper reason than you may think. There may not be a very fundamental difference between the memory in our brain, the memory in our plasma cells, and the memory in our entire body that knows how to let us be true to ourselves from day to day. Some work indicates that it takes about half an hour to build the source of a new protein—the necessary step toward producing antibody. On the other hand, it has been found that after sufficiently severe electric shock, a mammal will forget all events that preceded the shock by about half an hour and less. Here too, there is an indication that memory takes as long to establish itself as it takes to establish a new protein-forming structure.

You may think that the tremendous list of antigens that you have learned to fight must be paralleled with an equally long list of very differently backboned antibodies. But no: all of your antibodies belong to the class of gamma globulins, and they are all made up of two long chains called A-chains and two short ones called B-chains, all tied together with S-S bonds somewhat like this:

```
                              _____
                        B                S
                                         S
 _____
     A      S    S                            S
            S    S                            S
     A      _____       S
                                         S
                              _____
                              B
```

Without a B-chain, an A-chain will be inactive.

Still, there is one very great difference between two

groups of antibodies: the first molecules you make, upon your first contact with an antigen, will have a molecular weight of more than a million, but later, when you are exposed to the same antigen again and have become sensitized, you will form a new, much smaller kind of antibody and at a much higher rate. Just the fact that this secondary response is so much different from the first—no matter how much time has lapsed after that first contact—proves that the memory of your lymphocytes and plasma cells is very real, and very good. What form it has: actual antigen molecules, hiding for years encapsuled in an antibody molecule, or a bit of the nucleic acid system holding on to a code that only types out the antibody molecules when called for, nobody knows yet. There seems to be very little helical structure in the four-stranded thing I just sketched, so it is mostly made of "random coils," but as I indicated in the second chapter, such coils are not really random. They are like pretempered odd pieces of bent wire that can be stretched but will jump back into the same odd shape when allowed to relax. These two perhaps unbreakable ideas must then be reconciled: that the shape of a protein molecule in its natural surroundings is a direct result of the sequence of amino acid residues it is made of; and that every one of them must prefer to fit its A and B chains to one or at least only a very few of the thousands of haptens around it. Because somehow there must be a fit between antibody and antigen that is as good as that of a lock and key. Work with plasma cell cultures studied outside the body has given the impression that an antigen molecule, upon entering a plasma cell, interferes in such a way with the cell's metabolism and code system that from now on it will specialize in just that antibody which fits that antigen—as if the key that fits the lock has opened a closet full of the same locks. But not in all experiments have cells shown this rubber stamp-like behavior: many seem able to make several different antibodies. In a sensitized animal, the stamping or printing or whatever mechanism you want to call it, goes very fast: if you give the beast some radioactive amino acids first, and then the antigen, thirty minutes later it will have radioactive antibody in its plasma cells, and in another thirty minutes they will have been released into the bloodstream. One injection of antigen will start the formation of about one hundred thousand molecules of antibody per second, but as soon as all antigen has been bound by this explosive attack, the production of antibody stops. As soon as more antigen is added, more antibody is made again. This at least is the way the two are matched in cell cultures. In your body, the antibody that has not combined with antigen will live about as long as any other globulin molecules would: their half-life will be about fifteen days, or longer in animals that are larger, and shorter in animals that are smaller than you are.

You may get the impression from all this, that the interaction between antigen and antibody, no matter how complicated the events are that lead to it, is about as simple as a + b = c. I suppose sometimes it is, and I can well imagine how a bacterium will be choked by simply getting coated, but there is a whole train of events that can be started by such simple complex formations. When even as few as eight antibody molecules attach themselves to antigenic spots on a bacterium, for example, the bug suddenly becomes attractive to eosinophils and neutrophils, and will be eaten. Probably, the taste is provided not by the antibody itself, but by the tail end of a procession of other proteins, all called "complement." What has happened is this: when the antibody combined with the antigen, the event attracted a component of complement called C'1, which then changed into an enzyme that attacked and attracted other components of complement, the last one providing the main attraction for the white cells.

Measuring Antibody-Antigen Reactions

Even the combining of antibody with antigen in plasma, with no structure near them to hold on to, often traps or adsorbs, or (to use an official term) fixes complement. On the other hand, complement has a dramatic power when it can join the interaction between a blood group antigen and its antibody at the surface of a red cell: the complement will then make the cell hemolyse. This gives us a very nice chance to measure antibody-antigen reactions: the amount of complement such a reaction fixes and thus makes unavailable to lyse red cells with, should be an indication of how much antibody and antigen combined in the first place. You can probably design some tests with this principle, or even think of a machine to do the tests for you. They are complement fixation tests.

There are also simpler immunological systems that you can use well in a laboratory. Here is a nice test that Dr. Ratnoff uses to measure Factor XII (see Chapter I): purified human Factor XII is injected into a rabbit. The rabbit makes antibodies against it. Red cells of some mammal are collected, washed with isotonic salt solution, and treated to turn them into rather dead adsorbing particles. (In some similar tests, a suspension of latex particles is used.) Plasma from the rabbit is added and some anti-Factor XII antibody will go on the cells' surface. Now, to the coated (and again washed) red cells, plasma from a normal person is added. The abundant (or at least not absent) Factor XII molecules will rapidly attach themselves to the anti-XII antibody-coated cells, and the cells will agglutinate. Then you can repeat the test with serial dilutions of the normal plasma, and compare their agglutinating ability with the perhaps Factor XII-deficient plasma you are actually interested in. You can also create Factor XII-deficient plasma by simply dumping some of the rabbit plasma containing anti-XII into normal plasma and thus bind the normal Factor XII. All these tests are of course about as clean as the antibody is, and the purity of antibody the rabbit had formed depends directly on the purity of the protein you injected it with to start the whole thing. And then, antibodies are not always choosy enough; many will "cross-react" with proteins merely related to the one you injected.

Another trick is to plant drops of antibody solution in a plate of gel, all around a central drop of unknown protein. The solutions will then all slowly diffuse out toward each other, and where a front of known antibody meets the front of proteins coming from the central unknown drop and does find in it the antigen by which it was once created, a white zone of antibody-antigen will indicate the joyful recognition. In other words, if the white lines show up between the unknown central well and the wells around it that contained anti-x antibody and anti-y antibody respectively, then the unknown must contain the proteins x and y or some close relatives. Another trick is immune electrophoresis: the electrophoretic pattern of proteins (see page 52) is exposed to a gel containing antibody, and zones will appear where the diffusing antigens in the pattern meet the corresponding antibody. I am sure we can think of combinations of complement fixation, latex particle coating, radioisotope tagging, and gel techniques that will lead to very refined, and often very misleading, detection methods.

How all these forces are balanced and poised for action within you—that is quite another story. You can see a meaningful sequence in what you have read thus far: a bacterium enters; it releases a bit of antigen; the antigen is carried to a plasma cell; it penetrates; the cell switches its production to form antibody and releases it; the antibody travels to the bacterium and combines with the antigen, also adsorbing complement C'1 protein; this becomes an enzyme and reacts with other complement species, finally attracting the tasty one; a granulocyte rushes over and eats it all, then dies; a piece of its disintegrating cytoplasm is swallowed by a lymphocyte or plasma cell; more antibody is made; and so on. All this seems meaningful, because anything that saves your life must be. Yet, the more complex and life-size these processes are, the more we seem to take them for granted. Even the walk of a white cell to its prey can be looked down upon as something just natural for the cell to do: "After all, it has to eat to survive, doesn't it?" Does it want to, or is it just part of a mysterious plot within you, aimed to keep you alive?

VI

THE WHOLE

I feel I have given you a five-chapter-long introduction rather than a short book, a set of characters without a play. Most books about blood are like that: the elements as neatly separated as they should be for laboratory study, never to meet again as they should in life. As the components I gave you do play together within you, are they being moved by a common invisible force and toward a common purpose? We take for granted that their concerted efforts all lead toward better survival, but it is possible that they lead there or anywhere without aiming for anything. If you want to be biological about blood, say that the pattern formed by its inherited human components has a high survival value, merely since it survived better inside you than other patterns in the mammoth did. If you want to be teleological or theological, say that the aim to survive was there before survival itself. Either attitude, if you are curious enough, should encourage you to look for some connections between how you are living and why you are. You may then still come up with some general directions that life seems either destined, doomed, or desiring to take.

I think the most obvious property, the very nature even of life, seems to be its dedication to making simple matter more complicated, more and more structured, thereby opposing the physical laws that want lifeless matter to become less and less shaped, less organized, more chaotic. As a living thing, our brain can probably not help but believe that the more complex a given mass of matter is, the better. It is true that we also feel respect for a great mind that can reduce what had seemed like a complex mass of data to something that turns out to be simple, but that would only mean something that seemed chaotic and hard to memorize has been shown as a structure obeying certain simple rules: simplification means giving more structure, not less. A chair will look like a very complex structure if you force yourself to forget its purpose. It will appear a random arrangement of matter that could just as well have three legs instead of four. Cut this chaos in half and you will think you now have two of them and will have lost nothing, because you fail to see that all parts of the chair are bound together by their obedience to an external relationship, each part in its own way. You can compare such unity with that of a circle, undivisible, rather than a random line.

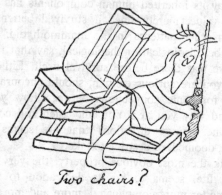

Two chairs?

FIGURE 55

I think it may help to introduce two words: a continuum, which would be a collection of completely identical elements, and a discontinuum, which would also be a whole, a collection, but of unidentical, varied elements. Divide a continuum, and you will have two of them; divide a discontinuum, and you will have two masses of random junk. A thing that we do not understand will appear a continuum, so that breaking it seems to cause no loss; only when we understand it as a discontinuum will we see the damage a division would do to it. Even without understanding it, we may be satisfied that some shape or event is a discontinuum if it repeats itself in space or in time, because then it gives evidence of having been created under the influence of some hidden law, that may some day be discovered. That is why scientists look for events that can be repeated or that repeat themselves even without our help. There are many: in our blood, the number of eosinophils and basophils undulates with day and night, our blood glucose wavers with our mealtimes, our blood pressure dances on our heartbeat.

All these recurrent events, together with the rather regular repetition of passage through liver, glands, kidneys, and intestinal walls, must create a very complex pattern of waves on top of waves on top of waves, a pattern that our body dictates to our blood. It is hard to judge how much or how little the blood benefits by these events, but it may be worthwhile to wonder if our blood could be better off without us. When you look at a neutrophil through the microscope, see it move as if it is sniffing around and then making up its mind to take off somewhere, and then if you remember that you are full of these tiny cells, you may wonder if they are not better off without your dictatorship and you may almost feel like setting the little things free: after all, who knows at what level of complexity further organization may become disastrous? Your bone marrow could just as successfully be planted in the banks and springs of some tropical river, sprouting its red cells, white cells, and platelets and letting them slowly run downstream, consuming oxygen drawn from the air, and devouring insects that would fall prey to the complex system of immune reactions, complement, phagocytosis, and memory. It would run down to spread out, a red current dying into the pale ocean no more aimlessly than many more organized people die in an aimless society. But on its way, and through the years of rain and drought and the changing of species living off it, the river would mutate and adjust itself to the needs of the world, because it is alive.

That would be no more surprising than the responsive way your blood behaves now, within you. It is true that your blood needs your heart to keep flowing, but your heart needs your blood as well: one coronary vessel occlusion can reduce oxygen supply to your heart muscle enough to make it stop and you will die, within minutes. Fifteen minutes of no blood flow, and your brain will break down to a useless mass. That shows you what urgency there is in some of the work the blood does for you. What are you doing for it? You are keeping it warm with the oxygen that it has to supply itself, at a temperature that it does not really need: it is stored better at four degrees Centigrade. It is your style of survival, not that of your blood, which demands a climate where enzyme reactions achieve a near-maximal speed. Quite possibly, if it could only stay cool, your blood would have less trouble keeping itself sterile and liquid.

If it is true that blood represents the old ocean water

we took along with us when we crawled onto the land, then I see nothing wrong with regarding it as a captive mass that somehow has had more and more tasks imposed upon it, and that has been trying to cope with them by mutating and evolving away from the rest of our body. While our muscles made myoglobin, our blood went on and made more complicated hemoglobin and then red cells to contain it. While our tissue cells still make thromboplastin when their cytoplasmic structure in them is disturbed, the way thrombocytes in more primitive animals' blood still may, our blood had to cut down on the cellular elements and reduce them to tiny platelets, meanwhile developing a very complex system of dissolved proteins that must be even more sensitive to touch than the old explosive thrombocytes were. The blood seems as plagued by improvements as a space program.

Of course, this approach to blood, as if it were a system that does not always get along too well with the ideas of its carrier, may be neither conventional nor realistic. Perhaps a more conventional way, and one that will lead to more conventional answers, is based on the presumption that our survival is the result of good cooperation among our various parts. For example, the rate of oxygen delivery to your tissues is only roughly regulated by the amount of red cells your blood can give you to work with. In anemia, too few red cells are available and the heart will pump harder to pass the same cells around more often. On the other hand, if your heart fails to work hard enough your blood is likely to make more cells, so that even on their slow passage they can exchange enough gas. Not a perfect solution in this case: the high number of red cells will make the blood more viscous and give the heart even more work to pump it around.

Just the plain flow of blood is not very plain and results from many interactions. The blood will pass through wide vessels more or less as a sleeve of plasma, platelets, and white cells with a faster-flowing filling of red cells in the center. I don't know what forces demand this orientation, but it may help in protecting the vessel walls against infection and damage: this way the white cells and platelets that do have this task will always be available without too much interference from the pushy red cells. In the capillaries, where only one cell can pass per instant per cross section, or to say it more simply, where cells have to pass in single file, the red cells will be pushed through like soft plungers and chase the plasma ahead of them (Figure 56). Nowhere does the blood flow as a homo-

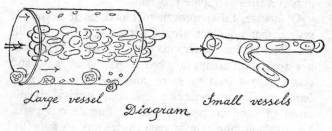

Large vessel   *Diagram*   *Small vessels*

FIGURE 56

geneous (so-called "Newtonian") fluid. Even in glass tubes, especially those of less than forty times the red cell diameter, it will not move according to simple physical laws, but more easily than expected. The higher the viscosity ("thickness") of the plasma is, the higher of course will be the viscosity of the whole blood, but this plasma effect is greater with higher hematocrits. In other words, something that makes plasma thicker will also increase the thickening effect of the added red cells. The presence of the red cells, on the other hand, will seem to have less and less effect the faster the blood flows, because above a certain rate of flow the cells will run more through the center of the tube away from the walls which will then only rub plasma. The apparent viscosity will then be less than expected, and probably resemble that in vivo. Apart from the differences that no one can measure yet, there are two between the flow of blood running through an artificial tube and its flow through your vessels: the heart pumps in spurts, and the blood vessels yield. The effects of pumping are complex. By yielding to pressure surges, the vessels reduce the apparent viscosity of the blood.

Functions of the Blood

One error in thinking of blood as a mixture flowing through tubes is that you tend to forget it is almost as intimately related with its world as city traffic is related with indoor city life. If you travel along with the blood and keep your eyes open for interchanges with the passing scenery, you will see soon enough how granulocytes go out into the tissues, lymphocytes go out and come back through the lymph, atoms such as iron are picked up by proteins and dropped in the liver or elsewhere, in the capsules and tubules of the kidneys harmful molecules of urea go out, and glucose goes out and comes back later; all along the road particles of broken-down cells and other junk are eaten by the cells of the reticulo-endothelium cells, platelets and broken red cells disappear in the spleen, hemoglobin is picked up by proteins, and dumped and broken down in the liver; passing pancreas, intestines, and other points of interest you may be showered with hormones, enzymes, digested food. One moment there is insulin all over, the next you are in the liver and suddenly many glucose molecules disappear, linked to become insoluble chains of glycogen, and so on.

One function of the blood, as you can read in any simple biology book, is to transport hormones from the glands that form them to the place where they must work. That sounds as if the blood knows where to go. In reality, neither the blood nor the hormones know where to go, and presumably all go everywhere; the wisdom must be in the tissues, who know how to respond in their own ways. Many may not answer out loud but may be as deeply affected as those who have been drawing our attention by their hysterical reactions. On the other hand, certain tissues and substances outside the blood may have a specific hunger for specific things. If you want to sound informed, you call them "pools." When the blood pool is overloaded with glucose, the glucose spills over in the urine pool. Granulocytes have at least two pools: blood and tissues. Lymphocytes have at least three: blood, lymph, and tissues. When heparin is injected into the blood, it disappears fast but appears to return later: it seems to have gone into the lymph for a while. Multiple pool systems provide pretty puzzles for mathematicians who study survival of cells and substances injected into the blood, but this kind of pool game should remind the biologist that nothing inside him lives alone, and that he is a pool of pooling pools.

Hemostasis

With a bit of added information I can give you one example of interactions: hemostasis, meaning whatever it is that makes your wounds stop bleeding. I choose it because it is the only one I am rather familiar with. The added information will be embedded in things you already met in all previous chapters, and now given in an ungrammatically brief style. I will not fall in the too-common trap of drawing scattered words on a large piece of paper and then connecting them with arrows, because such an aggressive form of art can only be intended to make the artist think and should never be performed in public. You can make your own tangled web of misdirections from the stuff that follows.

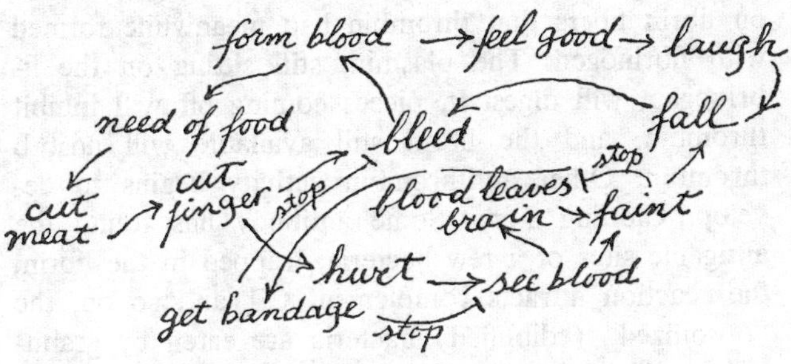

FIGURE 57

You have cut yourself with a dirty knife, while slicing a carrot. The metal, and with it some carrot cells and some bacteria, have gone through your skin cells, a bit of connective tissue, and the walls of some small blood vessels. Alarm, via your pituitary and adrenals, causes some increase in circulating fibrinogen and Factor VIII. Your blood is exposed to some tissue collagen: long, mostly helical, three-stranded protein molecules that probably force water into specific structures and, perhaps as a result, attract platelets specifically. The platelets liberate ADP (adenosine diphosphate, easily converted in the plasma to adenosine monophosphate with release of one phosphate and energy), and the ADP makes platelets stick together in clumps, then becomes harmless AMP. Meanwhile, tissue cells broken means thromboplastin formed; with prothrombin, Factor V (partially concentrated on platelet surfaces) and calcium ions it forms thrombin; thrombin makes platelets break and liberate phospholipid, hence more clotting started with adsorbed and concentrated factors on the phospholipid micelles will create more thrombin, and micelles may also activate Factor XII. Factor XII will then activate plasminogen so that it becomes plasmin, but most of the plasminogen will be on fibrin fibers that thrombin had meanwhile formed with fibrinogen. The plasmin, still sitting on the fibrinogen, will digest it, pieces coming off will inhibit thrombin, and the fibrin still available will adsorb thrombin. Other antithrombin activity begins to develop. Clotting stops. Some antibody has found the antigenic sites of a few bacteria, trapped in the fibrin; the reaction attracts complement C′1 and so on, the "opsonized" (ediblified) bacteria are eaten by granulocytes; fibrin is eaten by eosinophils, and so on, see under white cells. Plasmin also activates C′1.

The strangely accurate repair work that follows cannot be described in this book, but do not worry, your tiny bit of finger structure is already being repaired by the time you begin to feel slightly faint and decide to lie down for a moment. Not because you lost so much blood: your kidneys may not even have felt it and may not have made more erythropoietin yet. You are only flat on your back for the sheer survival value of it all: your blood pressure has dropped a bit, maybe because after the excitement in your adrenals died down, the system that inhibited them is still going, and now your brain is slightly short of oxygen. Keep your head low if you insist on uninterrupted reasoning.

Well, there you have it, the little book about blood. All that follows is just an appendix. As you will see, and as you saw so far, there is very little in this book about diseases. There are of course some very interesting ones. If you have one, see your doctor, not me. All I can give you is words, and in books yet! But first, a few more words of my own, because I suddenly find myself reluctant to let you go, and worried that I gave you too little. Frankly, all I wanted to give you is some curiosity and then some respect and love for the beauty of blood, yours, your loved one's, everyone's. Even to the murderer who knows nothing about blood, it is the most terrible flag protruding to accuse him. It should be better than that to us, if this book has been of any use. Still, no matter how deeply I am involved in blood, I can rather easily pour an unknown sample of it down the drain, while I will be very reluctant to spill one I have become familiar with, and not merely because it represents time well spent. The single drop of blood I have studied under the microscope, the single white cell I will have watched for more than half an hour becomes very dear to me, and darned if I don't catch myself trying to think of the most humane way to dispose of it. If every murder would have to take more than an hour and at such close range, none would be committed: no man can be an enemy when seen that near.

Of course I can have nothing against natural death; it is supposed to be as unavoidable as being born. Scientists insist that death is our, or at least their price for sex: when sperm and egg fuse and split again

She is full of it herself

Farewell Soma, you old bag of seawater!

FIGURE 58

they continue to exist in the form of newly created sperms or eggs, but the beautiful body they build around themselves (often called "soma") is only supposed to be an incidental carrier, needed to transport its fertile cargo safely to a proper time and place for the next fertilization. From this awfully diagrammatic viewpoint, man is little more than a pear that must be eaten to spread the seeds. Even more depressing is the belief that who eats must eventually be eaten. Kindly remember that when I am quite wrinkled I may still continue learning and telling my own well-grown seed what I learned; this is where I am ahead of any pear, and it is a grander form of eternity than the one our sperms and eggs enjoy, because theirs consists merely of parting a very rigidly coded form of information from generation to generation. The information our soma collects and passes on is much more adaptable (I hope).

I have seen death in many forms. I have seen protein solutions curdle over a Bunsen burner, white cells die of starvation in a sickening burst of bubbles, tissues dry in air and curl up, and I have seen people at war. It always seems the greater complex survives the smaller. There is a turnover of protein and lipids in the white cell: the cell survives its own molecules, because it produces new ones for old. And the myeloblast survives the granulocytes it makes, and you and your bone marrow survive the myeloblasts. But as you age, so do even the youngest cells in you, and thorough studies are now being made to find how blood cells born in an older body are "born older." If such changes will ever be prevented—who knows. Meanwhile, the best we can do is hope that as we survive our cells, mankind will survive us.

APPENDIX

A. Some Dates

There are now more scientists alive than dead. Every generation should therefore produce as much progress in science as had been produced in the eternity before it began its own work. No wonder we are approaching truth, or whatever it is, faster and faster; we seem about ready to crash-land on it, and soon we will be so overwhelmed with details that we shall only have time to give our own reports if we do not listen to others. The samplings below are intended to show some of this acceleration.

When	What	Who and Where
18,000 B.C.	Heart in mammoth correctly located, according to cave art.	Aurignac man, Spain
1000 B.C.	Difference in color between what is now known as arterial and venous blood.	Sumerians, Persia
400 B.C.	Collected blood separates in different layers, depending on disease (now known to be caused by red and then white cells sedimenting abnormally fast before blood has chance to clot).	Polybus, son-in-law of Hippocrates, Greece
300 B.C.	Blood flows through the veins, directed by valves.	Erasistratus, Antioch

A.D. 1553	Blood does not flow directly from one heart ventricle to the other, but via the lungs, where it is nourished by inspired air and becomes bright red.	M. Servetus, burned at stake for this view, Switzerland
1628	Motion of heart is cause of circulation.	W. Harvey, England
1649	First transfusion attempted.	Rev. F. Potter, England
1658	Red blood cells discovered.	J. Swammerdam, Holland
1661	Capillary circulation seen.	M. Malpighi, Italy
1666	Successful transfusion in dog and man.	R. Lower, England
1667	Man dies after repeated transfusions with sheep blood (of what is now known as immune reaction); transfusion is outlawed.	J. B. Dais, France
1674	Color of blood comes from red cells. Diameter of red cells measured.	A. van Leeuwenhoek, Holland
1700	Serum contains albumin, related to egg white.	H. Boerhaave, Holland
1749	White blood cells discovered.	J. Lieutaud, France
1777	Red cell shape, and its change in high and low salt concentration described. Also: clotting occurs in plasma only, not in cell part.	W. Hewson, England
1845	Blood clotting is enzymatic.	A. Buchanan, England
1850	Invisible fibrinogen is converted to fibrin. Thrombosis described.	R. Virchow, Russia
1852	An iron compound in red cells combines with carbon dioxide and with oxygen.	J. von Liebig, Germany
1868	Red cells are formed in bone marrow.	E. Neumann, Germany
1878	Staining of cells invented.	P. Ehrlich, Germany
1892	Prothrombin is converted to thrombin; thrombin converts fibrinogen to fibrin.	A. Schmidt, Germany
1900	Red cells of one person will clump with serum of certain other types of person (there are blood groups).	K. Landsteiner, Austria

1940–present. Almost all material in this book is collected from publications of the last twenty-five years or so.

B. Some Literature

There is only one book that I know as a general approach to blood. It is: *Functions of the Blood,* edited by R. G. MacFarlane and A. H. T. Robb-Smith (Academic Press, New York, 1961). I have not read any of the hundreds of popular books on related subjects such as heredity, biochemistry, microscopy, biology, and so on, which all overlap with blood.

If you want to have a general or specific idea of what is going on in any biological research, work your way through the weekly *Current Contents,* Chemical, Pharmaco-Medical, and Life Sciences issue, published by the Institute for Scientific Information, Philadelphia, Pennsylvania. It prints the contents listings given by most journals that have become available during the current week. Most journals appear monthly. The ones that print almost exclusively articles about blood and its circulation are listed below. Of course, much work is published in other journals, such as *Nature* and *Science* (two weeklies).

> *Acta Haematologica*
> *Bibliotheca Haematologica*
> *Blood*
> *Blut*
> *British Journal of Haematology*
> *Hémostase*
> *Immunology*
> *Journal of Immunology*
> *Journal of the Reticuloendothelial Society*
> *Nouvelle Revue Française d'Hématologie*
> *Review of Immunology*

Scandinavian Journal of Haematology
Thrombosis et Diathesis Haemorrhagica
Transfusion
Vox Sanguinis

American Heart Journal
American Journal of Cardiology
Angiologica
British Heart Journal
Circulation
Circulation Research
Japan Heart Journal

For more thorough alarm, look at the annually appearing *Federation Proceedings, Abstracts:* about three thousand abstracts of lectures given in one early spring week. Properly blended, they could quite possibly answer many questions that no one has even asked yet.

C. Some Sizes

To make proportions between unfamiliar sizes meaningful, you must translate them into familiar ones. The most dangerous way to do this is by threatening to place all subunits in question, such as your teeth, your red cells, or your protein molecules, end to end and then trying to tell you how far you are reaching. This is not only an unrealistic project; even if successful it may tell you nothing new. For example, just the bit of ink used in this dot · suffices to make a line that reaches to the end of our universe—try it out, but remember that the line must be infinitely narrow.

Only when surface area is the point of interest, as

it should be, does it pay to lay a body out, because it reminds you that living things do not contain any homogenized bulk, and that all of us are things within things within things, each thing with its peculiar skin, and the whole adding up to a tremendous amount of miscellaneous surface. I just figured out how much of the town I could paint red (or rather, pale transparent yellow) with your red cells, but I would not even tell you, because when I imagined this dream coming to life, I saw myself wondering, brush in hand, confronting the first house I came to: just the roof? Or the walls too, and indoors? How about the closet shelves? Nothing flat enough in this world to obey simple mathematics. Still, with the data listed below plus a few unlisted ones that you know (such as your height, and figures given in this book), you can come to your own and interesting conclusions.

Object	Molecular Weight	Longest Diameter, in Ångströms
Hydrogen molecule	2	2
Stearic acid molecule	284	24
Hemoglobin molecule	40,000	64
Prothrombin molecule	69,000	107
Cell membrane thickness		often about 100
Fibrinogen molecule	330,000	475
Blood platelet, human		about 20,000

1 inch = 25.4 mm.
1 mm = 1000 microns = 1,000,000 millimicrons = 10,000,000 Ångströms.

INDEX

A native of the Netherlands, Leo Vroman received his Masters degree from the Jakarta Medical College in Indonesia and his Ph.D. degree in animal physiology from Utrecht University, Holland. He has written many technical accounts of his research on surface contact effects on proteins of the blood and has also published volumes of his poetry, for which he was awarded the 1965 P. C. Hooft Prize from the Dutch government. A former Research Associate of the Department of Animal Behavior of The American Museum of Natural History, Dr. Vroman is now on the research staff of a Brooklyn hospital.